Creatures and Scary Things

ANTHOLOGY 3

Compiled by
Elspeth Graham and **Mal Peet**

OXFORD
UNIVERSITY PRESS

Contents

Stories by significant children's writers
Bill's New Frock *Anne Fine* 6
Nightmare Stairs *Robert Swindells* 7
Treasure Island *R. L. Stevenson* 8
Goodnight Mr Tom *Michelle Magorian* 10
Dracula *Bram Stoker* 12
Carrie's War *Nina Bawden* 14

Poems by significant children's writers
Jabberwocky (from *Through the Looking-glass*)
    Lewis Carroll 16
Humpty Dumpty Explains (from *Through the Looking-glass*)
    Lewis Carroll 17
The Wendigo *Ogden Nash* 19
On a Breezy Day *Iain Crichton Smith* 20
Rags *Judith Thurman* 20
Spill *Judith Thurman* 20
The Poet's Garden *Roger McGough* 21
A Small Dragon *Brian Patten* 22
My Last Dragon *Russell Hoban* 23
Running Lightly Over Spongy Ground *Theodore Roethke* 24
Distracted the Mother said to her Boy *Gregory Harrison* 25

Playscripts
    Twopence to Cross the Mersey *Helen Forrester*
        (adapted by Valerie Windsor) 26
    Skungpoomery *Ken Campbell* 30

Concrete poems
    Hippopotamus *Julie Holder* 34
    Flying Fish *Alan Riddell* 34

Wind *Eugene Gomringer* 35
Firework! *Mal Peet* 35
Avenue *Michael Gibbs* 35
Master of Disguise *Mal Peet* 35

Recounts
The Unsinkable Sinks 36
The Titanic Disaster Hearings
    edited by Tom Kuntz 37
A Night to Remember *Walter Lord* 39

Instructional texts
Fried Eggs *Mrs Beeton* 40
Chips *Nigel Slater* 41
Some of the Rules of Hockey 42
Harry Potter and the Philosopher's Stone *J. K. Rowling* 44

Myths, legends, and fables
The Torch *Jill Paton Walsh* 47
Two Men and a Bear *Aesop* 51
To Find a Son and Heir *Raymond Wilson* 52
The Egg Cracks 54
Beowulf *Rosemary Sutcliff* 55
Things that go Bump in the Night *Wilbur G. Howcroft* 58
King Arthur 60
   The Historie of King Arthur *Sir Thomas Malory* 60
   The Legend of King Arthur and his Knights *Sir James Knowles* 61
   The Sword in the Stone *T. H. White* 62
   King Arthur and the Round Table *Geraldine McCaughrean* 64

Classic and narrative poetry
From a Railway Carriage *R. L. Stevenson* 67
The Fox 68
The Spider and the Fly *Mary Howitt* 70
Cool Cat *Mike Jubb* 72

Non-chronological reports

The Private Life of the Otter *Jeremy Mallinson* 74
Dragons Around the World *David Passes* 76
A London Evacuee sees his First Cow *BBC News* 78
Tongue *Macmillan Encyclopedia* 79
Taste and Smell *Dorling Kindersley Science Encyclopedia* 80
Blood, Bones and Body Bits *Nick Arnold* 81

Explanation

The Silken Trap 82

Stories and poems from different cultures

When Hitler Stole Pink Rabbit *Judith Kerr* 84
The Cay *Theodore Taylor* 86
Walkabout *James Vance Marshall* 89
Picnic in Jammu *Zulfikar Ghose* 92
Slake's Limbo *Felice Holman* 94
Mum, Dad and Me *James Berry* 96

Choral/performance poetry

Hiawatha *H. W. Longfellow* 98
Hiawatha *adapted by Michael Bogdanov* 99
Storytime *Judith Nicholls* 102
The Cake That Makes you Scream *Dave Ward* 104

Persuasive writing

Letters 106
Looking Forward to a Better Future (leaflet)
   Friends of the Earth 108
Pure Magic (advert) 109
Second Sight (leaflet) *Mark Tully* 109
Old Macdonald had a farm ... (leaflet) *Animal Aid* 110
Chicken Brained *Miles Kington* 111

Introduction

This book is an anthology. If you look up the word in a dictionary, you will find that it means 'a collection of short pieces of writing'. The dictionary might also give you the derivation of the word – where it comes from. It comes from two Greek words: *anthos*, which means 'flower' and *logia*, which means 'collection'. The idea is that an anthology is a lovely bunch of 'word-flowers'.

Actually, there are not many flowers in this book. On page 21 there is a poet who tries to write about flowers, but he makes a complete mess of it. We do have a word-hippo though, and a word that explodes like a firework. You will also find in this anthology several dragons, a couple of fried eggs and a good helping of chips. You will meet a vampire and a pirate, and a policeman with no trousers. You will find out what an otter's house is called and how a spider spins its web. You will be cast away on a desert island and discover several spooky Australian things that go bump in the night, and you will also have a picnic in India. (There are some strange connections between these things, too. Look at the bottom of each page for this symbol and follow the clue to the pages where you can read more… Or you could look in the index on page 112.)

Writing is magical stuff because it can bring you all these things and because it can take you anywhere in the world. And you don't even have to get out of your chair. We hope you enjoy travelling around in this book. Most of all, we hope this book helps and encourages you to become a writer yourself.

Happy reading!

Mal Peet and Elspeth Graham

Bill's New Frock

ANNE FINE

1 A really awful start

When Bill Simpson woke up on
Monday morning, he found he
was a girl.

He was still standing staring
at himself in the mirror, quite
baffled, when his mother swept in.

'Why don't you wear this
pretty pink dress?' she said.

'I never wear dresses,' Bill burst out.

'I know,' his mother said. 'It's such a pity.'

And, to his astonishment, before he could even begin to
argue, she had dropped the dress over his head and zipped up
the back.

'I'll leave you to do up the shell buttons,' she said. 'They're a
bit fiddly and I'm late for work.'

And she swept out, leaving him staring in dismay at the
mirror. In it, a girl with his curly red hair and wearing a pretty
pink frock with fiddly shell buttons was staring back at him in
equal dismay.

'This can't be true,' Bill Simpson said to himself. 'This cannot
be true!'

He stepped out of his bedroom just as his father was rushing
past. He, too, was late in getting off to work.

Mr Simpson leaned over and planted a kiss on Bill's cheek.

'Bye, Poppet,' he said, ruffling Bill's curls. 'You look very sweet
today. It's not often we see you in a frock, is it?'

Nightmare Stairs

ROBERT SWINDELLS

Chapter One

Here's a riddle:

> *No vampire, ghost nor bug-a-boo*
> *I live and breathe and play, like you*
> *Yet I was murdered long ago*
> *Now tell me – how can this be so?*

Not easy, right? True though – every word. If you're not doing anything special I'll tell you all about it but I have to warn you – it's weird. Seriously weird.

Listen.

Treasure Island

ROBERT LOUIS STEVENSON

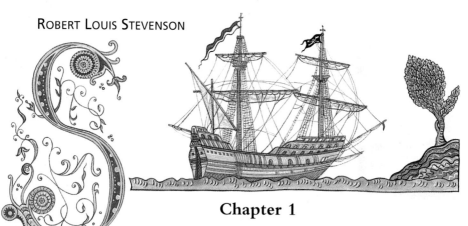

Chapter 1

Squire Trelawney, Dr Livesey, and the rest of these gentlemen having asked me to write down the whole particulars about Treasure Island, from the beginning to the end, keeping nothing back but the bearings of the island, and that only because there is still treasure not yet lifted, I take up my pen in the year of grace 17—, and go back to the time when my father kept the "Admiral Benbow" inn, and the brown old seaman, with the sabre cut, first took up his lodging under our roof.

I remember him as if it were yesterday, as he came plodding to the inn door, his sea-chest following behind him in a hand-barrow; a tall, strong, heavy, nut-brown man; his tarry pigtail falling over the shoulders of his soiled blue coat; his hands ragged and scarred, with black, broken nails; and the sabre cut across one cheek, a dirty, livid white. I remember him looking round the cove and whistling to himself as he did so, then breaking out in that old sea-song that he sang so often afterwards:

"Fifteen men on the dead man's chest —
Yo-ho-ho, and a bottle of rum!"

Goodnight Mr Tom

MICHELLE MAGORIAN

'Yes,' said Tom bluntly, on opening the front door. 'What d'you want?'

A harassed middle-aged woman in a green coat and felt hat stood on his step. He glanced at the armband on her sleeve. She gave him an awkward smile.

'I'm the Billeting Officer for this area,' she began.

'Oh yes, and what's that got to do wi' me?'

She flushed slightly. 'Well, Mr, Mr...'

'Oakley. Thomas Oakley.'

'Ah, thank you, Mr Oakley.' She paused and took a deep breath. 'Mr Oakley, with the declaration of war imminent ...'

Tom waved his hand. 'I knows all that. Git to the point. What d'you want?' He noticed a small boy at her side.

'It's him I've come about,' she said. 'I'm on my way to your village hall with the others.'

'What others?'

She stepped to one side. Behind the large iron gate which stood at the end of the graveyard were a small group of children. Many of them were filthy and very poorly clad. Only a handful had a blazer or coat. One tiny dark-haired girl in the front was hanging firmly on to a new teddy-bear.

The woman touched the boy at her side and pushed him forward.

'There's no need to tell me,' said Tom. 'It's obligatory and it's for the war effort.'

'You are entitled to choose your child, I know', began the woman apologetically.

Tom gave a snort.

'But,' she continued, 'his mother wants him to be with

someone who's religious or near a church. She was quite adamant. Said she would only let him be evacuated if he was.'

'Was what?' asked Tom impatiently.

'Near a church.'

Tom took a second look at the child. The boy was thin and sickly-looking, pale with limp sandy hair and dull grey eyes.

'His name's Willie,' said the woman.

Willie, who had been staring at the ground, looked up. Round his neck, hanging from a piece of string, was a cardboard label. It read 'William Beech'.

Tom was well into his sixties, a healthy, robust, stockily-built man with a head of thick white hair. Although he was of average height, in Willie's eyes he was a towering giant with skin like coarse, wrinkled brown paper and a voice like thunder.

He glared at Willie. 'You'd best come in,' he said abruptly.

The woman gave a relieved smile. 'Thank you so much,' she said, and she backed quickly away and hurried down the tiny path towards the other children. Willie watched her go.

'Come on in,' repeated Tom harshly. 'I ent got all day.'

Nervously, Willie followed him into a dark hallway. It took a few seconds for his eyes to adjust from the brilliant sunshine he had left to the comparative darkness of the cottage. He could just make out the shapes of a few coats hanging on some wooden pegs and two pairs of boots standing below.

'S'pose you'd best know where to put yer things,' muttered Tom, looking up at the coat rack and then down at Willie. He scratched his head. 'Bit 'igh fer you. I'd best put in a low peg.' ■

 There is more about evacuees on pages 14 and 78.

11

Dracula

Bram Stoker

Jonathan Harker, a young lawyer, has been sent on a business trip to Transylvania. This is an extract from his journal, describing his first meeting with his client – Count Dracula.

His face was a strong – a very strong – aquiline, with high bridge of the thin nose and peculiarly arched nostrils; with lofty domed forehead, and hair growing scantily round the temples, but profusely elsewhere. His eyebrows were very massive, almost meeting over the nose, and with bushy hair that seemed to curl in its own profusion. The mouth, so far as I could see it under the heavy moustache, was fixed and rather cruel-looking, with peculiarly sharp white teeth; these protruded over the lips, whose remarkable ruddiness showed astonishing vitality in a man of his years. For the rest, his ears were pale and at the tops extremely pointed; the chin was broad and strong, and the cheeks firm though thin. The general effect was one of extraordinary pallor.

Hitherto I had noticed the backs of his hands as they lay on his knees in the firelight, and they had seemed rather white and fine; but seeing them now close to me, I could not but notice that they were rather coarse – broad, with squat fingers. Strange to say, there were hairs in the centre of the palm. The nails were long and fine, and cut to a sharp point. As the Count leaned over me and his hands touched me, I could not repress a shudder. It may have been that his breath was rank, but a horrible feeling of nausea came over me, which, do what I would, I could not conceal. The Count, evidently noticing it, drew back; and with a grim sort of smile, which showed more than he had yet done his

protuberant teeth, sat himself down again on his own side
of the fireplace. We were both silent for a while; and as I
looked towards the window I saw the first dim streak of the
coming dawn. There seemed a strange stillness over
everything; but as I listened I heard, as if from down below
in the valley, the howling of many wolves.

 There is more about myths on page 54.

Carrie's War

Nina Bawden

> Carrie Willow and her brother Nick are World War Two evacuees. They
> have been sent to Wales where they have been taken in by Miss Evans
> and her brother. Here, they meet Mr Evans for the first time.

He wasn't an Ogre, of course. Just a tall, thin, cross man with a
loud voice, pale, staring, pop-eyes, and tufts of spiky hair sticking
out from each nostril.

Councillor Samuel Isaac Evans was a bully. He bullied his sister.
He even bullied the women who came into his shop, selling them
things they didn't really want to buy and refusing to stock things
that they did. 'Take it or leave it,' he'd say. 'Don't you know there's
a war on?'

He would have bullied the children if he had thought they were
frightened of him. But although Carrie was a little frightened, she
didn't show it, and Nick wasn't frightened at all. He was frightened
of Ogres and spiders and crabs and cold water and the dentist and
dark nights, but he wasn't often frightened of people. Perhaps this
was only because he had never had reason to be until he met Mr
Evans, but he wasn't afraid of him, even after that first, dreadful
night, because Mr Evans had false teeth that clicked when he
talked. 'You can't really be scared of someone whose teeth might
fall out,' he told Carrie.

The possibility fascinated him from the beginning, from the
moment Mr Evans walked into the kitchen while they were having
breakfast their first morning and bared those loose teeth in what he
probably thought was a smile. It looked to the children more like the
kind of grin a tiger might give before it pounced on its prey. They
put down their porridge spoons and stood up, politely and meekly.

It seemed to please him. 'You've got a few manners, I see. That's something! That's a bit of sugar on the pill!'

They didn't know what to say to this so they said nothing and he stood there, grinning and rubbing his hands together. At last he said, 'Sit down, then, finish your breakfast, what are you waiting for? It's a wicked Sin to let good food get cold. You've fallen on your feet, let me tell you, you'll get good food in this house. So no faddiness, mind! No whining round my sister for titbits when my back's turned. Particularly the boy. I know what boys are! Walking stomachs! I told her, you fetch two girls now, there's just the one room, but she got round me, she said, the boy's only a babby!' He looked sharply at Nick. 'Not too much of a babby, I hope. No wet beds. That I won't stand!'

Nick's gaze was fixed on Mr Evans's mouth. 'That's a rude thing to mention,' he said in a clear icy voice that made Carrie tremble. But Mr Evans didn't fly into the rage she'd expected. He simply looked startled – as if a worm had just lifted its head and answered him back, Carrie thought.

He sucked his teeth for a minute. Then said, surprisingly mildly, 'All right. All right, then. You mind your P's and Q's, see, and I won't complain. As long as you toe the chalk line! Rules are made to be kept in this house, no shouting, or running upstairs, and no Language.' Nick looked at him and he went on – quickly, as if he knew what was coming, 'No *Bad* Language, that is. I'll have no foul mouths here. I don't know how you've been brought up but this house is run in the Fear of the Lord.

 There is more about evacuees on pages 10 and 78.

Jabberwocky

LEWIS CARROLL

In *Through the Looking-glass,* Alice finds a book
with a strange poem in it.

'Twas brillig, and the slithy toves
Did gyre and gimble in the wabe;
All mimsy were the borogroves,
And the mome raths outgrabe.

'Beware the Jabberwock, my son!
The jaws that bite, the claws that catch!
Beware the Jubjub bird, and shun
The frumious Bandersnatch!'

He took his vorpal sword in hand:
Long time the manxome foe he sought –
So rested he by the Tumtum tree,
And stood awhile in thought.

And as in uffish thought he stood,
The Jabberwock, with eyes of flame,
Came whiffling through the tulgey wood,
And burbled as it came!

One, two! One two! And through and through
the vorpal blade went snicker-snack!
He left it dead, and with its head
He went galumphing back.

'And hast thou slain the Jabberwock?
Come to my arms, my beamish boy!
O frabjous day! Callooh! Callay!'
He chortled in his joy.

There is more about monsters on pages 19, 55 and 58.

Humpty Dumpty Explains

Later on in *Through the Looking-glass*, Alice meets Humpty Dumpty who is, as you'd expect, a bit of a big-head.

'You seem very clever at explaining words, Sir,' said Alice. 'Would you kindly tell me the meaning of the poem called *Jabberwocky?*'

'Let's hear it,' said Humpty Dumpty. 'I can explain all the poems that ever were invented – and a good many that haven't been invented just yet.'

This sounded very hopeful, so Alice repeated the first verse:

'Twas brillig, and the slithy toves
Did gyre and gimble in the wabe;
All mimsy were the borogroves,
And the mome raths outgrabe.

'That's enough to begin with,' Humpty Dumpty interrupted: 'there are plenty of hard words there. *Brillig* means four o'clock in the afternoon – the time when you begin *broiling* things for dinner.'

'That'll do very well,' said Alice: 'and *slithy?*'

'Well *slithy* means "lithe and slimy". "Lithe" is the same as "active". You see, it's like a portmanteau – there are two meanings packed up into one word.'

'I see it now,' Alice remarked thoughtfully: 'and what are *toves?*'

'Well *toves* are something like badgers – they're

17

something like lizards – and they're something like corkscrews.'

'They must be very curious-looking creatures.'

'They are that,' said Humpty Dumpty: 'also they make their nests under sun-dials – also they live on cheese.'

'And what's to *gyre* and *gimble*?'

'To *gyre* is to go round and round like a gyroscope. To *gimble* is to make holes like a gimblet.'

'And the *wabe* is the grass plot round a sun-dial, I suppose?' said Alice, surprised at her own ingenuity.

'Of course it is. It's called *wabe*, you know, because it goes a long way before it, and a long way behind it –'

'And a long way beyond it on each side,' Alice added. ▪

broiling: grilling
portmanteau: a small hinged case which opens like a book,
    so you can pack both sides
gyroscope: a ring mounted in a frame which spins in all directions
gimblet (gimlet): a sharp tool for boring holes

The Wendigo

OGDEN NASH

The Wendigo,
 The Wendigo!
  Its eyes are ice and indigo!
  Its blood is rank and yellowish!
   Its voice is hoarse and bellowish!
    Its tentacles are slithery,
     And scummy,
      Slimy,
       Leathery!
        Its lips are hungry blubbery,
         And smacky,
          Sucky,
           Rubbery!

    The Wendigo,
     The Wendigo!
      I saw it just a friend ago!
       Last night it lurked in Canada;
        Tonight on your veranda!
         As you are lolling hammockwise
          It contemplates you stomachwise.
           You loll,
            It contemplates,
             It lollops.
              The rest is merely gulps and gollops.

 There is more about monsters on pages 16, 55 and 58.

On a Breezy Day

IAIN CRICHTON SMITH

On a breezy day
the curtains swell at the window
like white ghosts
that are struggling to get out.

Rags

JUDITH THURMAN

The night wind
rips a cloud sheet
into rags,

then rubs, rubs
the October moon
until it shines
like a brass doorknob.

Spill

JUDITH THURMAN

the wind scatters
a flock of sparrows –
a handful of small change
spilled suddenly
from the cloud's pocket.

The Poet's Garden

ROGER MCGOUGH

The garden is looking particularly all right at
this time of the year. There are yellow things
everywhere and sort of red bits in
waving clumps. The lawn is as
green as grass and studded
with delicate little yellow
and white studs. Flowers,
I think they are called.

A Small Dragon

BRIAN PATTEN

I've found a small dragon in the woodshed.
Think it must have come from deep inside a forest
because it's damp and green and leaves
are still reflecting in its eyes.

I fed it on many things, tried grass,
the roots of stars, hazel-nut and dandelion,
but it stared up at me as if to say, I need
foods you can't provide.

It made a nest among the coal,
not unlike a bird's but larger,
it is out of place here
and is quite silent.

If you believed in it I would come
hurrying to your house to let you share my wonder,
but I want instead to see
if you yourself will pass this way.

There is more about dragons on pages 23, 76 and 102.

My Last Dragon

RUSSELL HOBAN

Forlorn he sits, and still forlorner,
alone and sad in his dark corner.
I said I'd write, I said I'd phone
but still he sits there all alone;
no one knows where to find him.

His scales are dull, his eyes are dim,
no fiery breath comes out of him;
all silent is his echoing roar,
his wings bear him aloft no more –
his battles are behind him.

I left him when at childhood's end
I waved to him as round the bend
of time he grew quite small, so small
that soon he wasn't there at all
except in memory.

 There is more about dragons on pages 22, 76 and 102.

Running Lightly Over Spongy Ground

THEODORE ROETHKE

Running lightly over spongy ground,
Past the pastures of flat stones,
The three elms,
The sheep strewn on a field,
Over a rickety bridge
Toward the quick-water, wrinkling and rippling.

Hunting along the river,
Down among the rubbish, the bug-riddled foliage,
By the muddy pond-edge, by the bog-holes,
By the shrunken lake, hunting, in the heat of summer.

The shape of a rat?
  It's bigger than that.
  It's less than a leg
  And more than a nose,
  Just under the water
  It usually goes.

  Is it soft like a mouse?
  Can it wrinkle its nose?
  Could it come in the house
  On the tips of its toes?

Take the skin of a cat
And the back of an eel,
Then roll them in grease,—
That's the way it would feel.

It's sleek as an otter
With wide webby toes,
Just under the water
It usually goes.

Turn to page 74 to find out about otters.

24

Distracted the Mother said to her Boy

GREGORY HARRISON

Distracted the mother said to her boy
'Do you try to upset and perplex and annoy?
Now, give me four reasons – and don't play the fool –
Why you shouldn't get up and get ready for school.'

Her son replied slowly, 'Well, mother, you see,
I can't stand the teachers and they detest me;
And there isn't a boy or a girl in the place
That I like or, in turn, that delights in my face.

'And I'll give you two reasons,' she said, 'Why you ought
Get yourself off to school before you get caught;
Because, first, you are forty and, next, you young fool,
It's your job to be there.
You're the head of the school.'

 There is more about comic authority figures on page 30.

Twopence to Cross the Mersey

HELEN FORRESTER, ADAPTED BY VALERIE WINDSOR

> In the 1930s the Forrester family fell on hard times. They left their comfortable house in the south of England and went to Liverpool, where the parents looked for work. Twelve-year-old Helen had to stay off school and look after her young sister and baby brother.

Scene Twelve

When the lights come up the rooms are empty except for Helen, Avril and the baby. Helen is wrapping the baby up in his dirty blanket, ready to lay him in the pram.

HELEN	(*narrating*) In the morning they were both up and out early. My father gave me a shilling as usual to buy the day's food. (*She pulls on a holey cardigan.*)
AVRIL	Are we going out?
HELEN	Yes.
AVRIL	(*peering into the pram*) Is he ill? He doesn't cry any more, does he, like proper babies do.
HELEN	I think it's because he's hungry. I suppose I'd better feed him before we go. I'll just run down and see if I can catch the milkman.

Helen sits Avril on the settee and then runs downstairs. Mrs Foster's brother is playing his piano, and the piano music continues in uninterrupted snatches until the end of the scene.

HELEN	(narrating as she goes) It wasn't enough ... the one pint of milk we could afford. Poor little Edward was slowly starving.
MRS FOSTER	(poking her head round her door) Is that you Helen Forrester? I've had complaints about that pram of yours on the stairs.
HELEN	Yes, Mrs Foster. Sorry.
MRS FOSTER	Can't you learn to walk down them stairs more ladylike?
HELEN	I want to catch the milkman.
MRS FOSTER	Too late. He's been.

*She shuts her door. **Helen** sees two bottles of milk on the doorstep. She stares at them for a moment, looks up and down to see whether anyone is watching, and then pounds up the stairs again.*

MRS FOSTER'S BROTHER'S VOICE Will you shut that racket on them stairs!

Helen takes two cracked mugs and fills one with water.

AVRIL	What are you doing?
HELEN	Ssh. Wait.

*Helen runs downstairs. Outside the front door, she hurriedly pours milk from each bottle into the empty mug, and then fills up the bottles with water. She shakes the bottle and replaces the cardboard tops. A **young policeman** has just turned the corner into the street. He stops and watches her. She is unaware of him. Finally, she hurries upstairs again. Her hands are trembling.*

AVRIL	What were you doing?
HELEN	Come on, quickly. We've got to go out.

*Helen puts the milk into a saucepan and covers it. Then she bumps the pram downstairs. Outside the **policeman** is examining the milk bottles. Then some **girls** run into the street and start playing. He moves back into the shadows.*

MRS FOSTER'S VOICE   Helen Forrester, I've warned you.

Helen pushes the pram out of the front door. Once outside, she breathes a sigh of relief.

HELEN   *(narrating)* Now I could buy the usual daily pint at the corner shop and Edward could have another two feeds.

*Helen pushes the pram out of sight. The **young policeman** follows her. The **girls** give up their game and wander off. **Helen** reappears with the pram and stops at a shop.*

HELEN   Now, then, we want milk, don't we, and bread. Two pounds of potatoes. And what shall we have? A pennyworth of marg or a pennyworth of bacon pieces?

*The **young policeman** is now right behind her.*

POLICEMAN Nice baby you've got there.
HELEN   *(jumping with fright)* Oh! Um ... yes.
POLICEMAN What's his name?
HELEN   *(becoming increasingly nervous)* Edward.
POLICEMAN *(surprised by her accent)* Edward? That's a nice name. And what's yours?
HELEN   Helen, Helen Forrester.
POLICEMAN And where's your Mam, Helen?
HELEN   She's out looking for work. So's Daddy.
POLICEMAN I see. From somewhere down south, are you?
HELEN   Yes.
POLICEMAN Any more brothers and sisters?
HELEN   They're all at school.
POLICEMAN I see. Well, you'd better get on, love. You'll catch cold. You shouldn't be outside in just a cardigan in this weather.

*Nervously, **Helen** goes into the shop. The **policeman** watches her go, and then walks away.*

HELEN   *(narrating)* The following morning, an extraordinary thing happened. A pint of milk was delivered at the top of our staircase. The milkman insisted it was for Edward and was sent by a friend. 'What friend?' I said. 'We haven't got any friends any more.' But he wouldn't say. For two long years he climbed our stairs and deposited the daily pint of milk.

Years later the shopkeeper told my mother about the young policeman who'd come into the shop asking questions about us, and who'd then apparently gone round to the dairy and ordered a daily pint of milk for Edward to be paid for out of his own meagre wages. I don't think there's any doubt that it saved Edward's life.

The piano music continues as the lights fade. ■

Skungpoomery

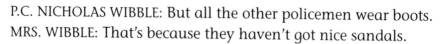

KEN CAMPBELL

Act One

Scene One

P.C. NICHOLAS WIBBLE: But all the other policemen wear boots.

MRS. WIBBLE: That's because they haven't got nice sandals.

WIBBLE: Well why've I always got to be different?

MRS. WIBBLE: It's not a case of 'being different', Nicholas, it's a case of being sensible. It's unhealthy to have your feet laced up inside those big clumping boots all day in hot weather –

WIBBLE: O Mum.

MRS. WIBBLE: I don't want to hear any more about it, Nicholas.

WIBBLE: Anyway those sandals pinch my feet, Mum.

MRS. WIBBLE: Nicholas! You little fibber! We got those sandals at Clarks and we both looked down the X-Ray machine together and we both saw that you had plenty of room in those sandals. Nicholas!

WIBBLE: Wh-at?

MRS. WIBBLE: What's that?

WIBBLE: What's what?

MRS. WIBBLE: On your tie?

WIBBLE: Nothing.

MRS. WIBBLE: Egg dribblings. Look at that. And I all nicely ironed it yesterday morning and now you've dribbled your egg on it. Come here. (*She leads him by his tie to the bowl and cloth.*)

WIBBLE: O Mum.

MRS. WIBBLE: O and it's not coming out look. It'll have to be put in soak.

WIBBLE: Oh no, Mum – look I'm due on the beat in five minutes. I can't wait while you soak it.

MRS. WIBBLE: Well I'm certainly not letting you go out with your tie in that state.

WIBBLE: The Sergeant gets really cross if I'm late.

MRS. WIBBLE: Well you'll just have to wear your bow-tie.

WIBBLE: O no.

MRS. WIBBLE: Nicholas!

WIBBLE: O look all the other policemen wear ordinary straight ties.

MRS. WIBBLE: Come here and let's put it on you and have less of your nonsense. Your Aunty Glad gave you this nice bow tie – and did you write her a proper thank you letter?

WIBBLE: Yes.

MRS. WIBBLE: Good boy. *(Looking at his face.)* Hanky? *(He supplies it.)* Lick.

He licks it and she wipes a bit of dirt off his face with it.

WIBBLE: 'Bye then, Mum.

MRS. WIBBLE: Kiss please. I've done you some sandwiches.

WIBBLE: O Mum, can't I eat in the canteen with the other policemen?

MRS. WIBBLE: O you make me so cross, Nicholas. We've just managed to nearly get rid of all your spots and now you want to go into that nasty canteen and eat greasy fried stuff.

WIBBLE: It's not all greasy fried stuff in there, Mum.

MRS. WIBBLE: You're an ungrateful boy, Nicholas.

WIBBLE: O I'm not ungrateful at all, Mum. I'm grateful. I really am. It's all right. I'll take the sandwiches. And I'll enjoy them.

MRS. WIBBLE: I should think so. O Nicholas! I ironed those trousers at the weekend and now look at them. They're all baggy at the knees. Don't you hitch them up when you sit down?

WIBBLE: Yes.

MRS. WIBBLE: Take them off and let me give them a quick press.

WIBBLE: O no, Mum – look I'm going to be ever so late now.

MRS. WIBBLE: Take them off, Nicholas, it won't take a moment.

WIBBLE: No.

MRS. WIBBLE: Nicholas!!!

WIBBLE: Oooooooooooh! *(Stamp and paddy. MRS. WIBBLE waits. He sulkily removes his trousers revealing Chilprufe underpants.) MRS. WIBBLE takes the trousers off and returns with an iron and ironing board.*

MRS. WIBBLE: Right.

WIBBLE: Please hurry up, Mum.

MRS. WIBBLE: I'm being as quick as I can, Nicholas. *(She is now ironing.)* The number of times I've been on to you, Nicholas, to just think before you go to bed at night, what you're going to need in the morning, and go over it and check it's all right then; there's absolutely no need for this breakfast time misery. But you, you never seem to know what you're at or what you're doing. *(The phone rings. She answers the iron, holding it next to her ear.)* Hello? Hello? Yahhhhhhhhhhhhhhhhhh! *(In her agony, she puts the iron down on the trousers.)* Butter! Get the butter, Nicholas!

WIBBLE: Oh yes, here you are. *(He shoves a full round soft marge pack onto his Mum's ear. They tie the pack to her ear with a scarf.)*

MRS. WIBBLE: Nicholas, you will be the death of me!

WIBBLE: How's it my fault, Mum. If you stick the iron in your ear.

MRS. WIBBLE: Nicholas, just shut up! *(Clouts him.)* Ooooof. *(The pain of the burn.)* Go and answer it.

WIBBLE: *(picking up the phone)* That's all right. That's not so good. That's very good. That's just first class. That's awful. That's good. That's rotten.

MRS. WIBBLE: Who is it?

WIBBLE: It's Auntie Glad. She wanted some help sorting out her tomatoes. O no! O Mum look what you've done now! *(He picks up the trousers revealing a huge burn hole.)* O no.

MRS. WIBBLE: I'm not the least bit sympathetic, Nicholas. It's just a direct result of your own thoughtlessness.

WIBBLE: What am I going to do now?

MRS. WIBBLE: Well you'll just have to wear your shorts.

WIBBLE: O no!

MRS. WIBBLE: They're in the airing cupboard.

WIBBLE: I can't wear short trousers on the beat, Mum!

 There is more about comic authority figures on page 25.

Hippopotamus

JULIE HOLDER

If you sat on a Hippo would it slop about like a water bed would it wobble like a water-filled balloon? Would it feel sticky like a jelly if you stroked it? Would it dent like a water logged sponge if you poked it? Would it burst if it crashed? If you smacked it would it splash? When they open mouths that wide does the river rush inside like a whirlpool? Together Hippos wallow Hippopotamoes in a stew. They dance on river beds like submarines with legs. They fight like battleships. They moo like cannons booming. They eat like horses and make noises in the water like giant whoopee cushions.

Flying Fish

ALAN RIDDELL

Wind

EUGENE GOMRINGER

```
            w         w
        d         i
      n       n       n
    i       d       i       d
  w                   w
```

Master of Disguise

MAL PEET

```
c d f b n s t v e
d h g h b s f r t
s x a d r d t p r
a p c m l c d s n
j s v t e f h o l
i g u w b l q u m
r z f y l h e g s
w r l o p c v o c
a s d o l m r g n
```

Avenue

MICHAEL GIBBS

treestreetree
treestreetree
treestreetree
treestreetree
treestreetree
treestreetree
treestreetree
treestreetree
treestreetree
treestreetree
treestreetree
treestreetree
treestreetree
treestreetree
treestreetree
treestreetree
treestreetree
treestreetree
treestreetree
treestreetree
treestreetree
treestreetree
treestreetree
treestreetree
treestreetree
treestreetree
treestreetree

Firework!

MAL PEET

```
r
o
m
a
n
c
a
n
d
l
e
!
```

35

The Unsinkable Sinks

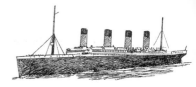

The S.S. *Titanic* left Southampton on her maiden voyage to New York at midday on the 10th of April 1912. It was the biggest and most luxurious ship that had ever existed. It was 269 metres long, and was the ultimate in marine design. Its massive steel hull was divided into sixteen watertight compartments; it was thought to be unsinkable. Among the First-Class passengers on this voyage were some of the richest people of Europe and the United States; their combined wealth has been estimated at some $250 million. For such passengers, the *Titanic* provided every convenience and comfort – including the first-ever onboard swimming pool. The ship was also equipped with the most up-to-date communications device, the Marconi radio telegraph.

It was this radio telegraph which warned the *Titanic's* Captain, Edward Smith, of the presence of icebergs. The warning came on the night of the 12th of April. The ship was then steaming through the icy North Atlantic several hundred kilometres south of Newfoundland. At 11.40 pm, Frederick Fleet, who was on look-out duty in the crow's-nest, saw a vast shape looming out of the darkness directly ahead of the ship. He telephoned a warning to the ship's bridge; but for many anxious seconds the ship remained on a collision course with the iceberg. At last the *Titanic* swung to port, and the huge ship slid past the towering hill of ice – so close that chunks of ice fell onto the deck.

To Frederick Fleet it seemed like a near miss. He was wrong. The iceberg had ripped a 90-metre long gash in the hull below the water-line. To one of the passengers, it seemed as if the ship 'had rolled over a thousand marbles'.

Two and a half hours later, the 'unsinkable' ship plunged beneath the freezing water. During that time, some passengers remained calm – some even continued to play cards on crazily-tilting tables. Elsewhere, there was panic as people fought for places in the lifeboats or threw themselves into the sea.

Of the 2,200 people on board the *Titanic*, approximately 1,500 died.

As dawn broke on the 13th, the liner *Carpathia* arrived on the scene and took on board 705 survivors.

The *Titanic* had enough lifeboats to hold fewer than half its passengers; even so, when the *Carpathia* arrived some of these boats were less than half-full.

The *Titanic* Disaster Hearings

EDITED BY TOM KUNTZ

This extract is from an American inquiry, investigating why the *Titanic* disaster happened. Herbert Pitman, an officer on the ship, was in command of one of the lifeboats. He is being questioned by Senator Smith.

MR PITMAN: As soon as she (the *Titanic*) disappeared, I said 'Now, men, we will pull toward the wreck.' Everyone in my boat said it was a mad idea because we had better save what few we had in my boat than to go back to the scene of the wreck and be swamped by the crowds that were there.

SENATOR SMITH: As a matter of fact, do you not know that your boat would have accommodated 20 or 25 more people?

PITMAN: A few more, yes, certainly.

SMITH: According to the testimony of your fellow officers –

PITMAN: My boat would have held more.

SMITH: *(continuing)* Your boat would have held about 60 or 65 people.

PITMAN: About 60.

SMITH: Tell us about your fellow passengers on that lifeboat. You say they discouraged you from returning or going in the direction of the cries?

PITMAN: They did. I told my men to get their oars out and pull toward the scene of the wreck.

SMITH: Yes?

PITMAN: I said 'We may be able to pick up a few more.'

SMITH: Who disagreed with that?

PITMAN: The whole crowd in my boat. A great number of them did.

SMITH: Women?

PITMAN: I could not tell whether women or men. They said it was rather a mad idea.

SMITH: I ask you if any woman in your boat appealed to you to return to the direction from which the cries came?

PITMAN: No-one.

SMITH: You say that no woman in your boat urged you to return?

PITMAN: None.

SMITH: The men with the oars?

PITMAN: They started to obey my orders … They commenced pulling towards the ship, and the passengers in my boat said it was a mad idea on my part to pull back to the ship, because if I did we should be swamped by the crowd that was in the water, and it would add another 40 to the list of drowned. I decided I would not pull back.

SMITH: Then did you turn the boat away from the wreck again?

PITMAN: No; just simply took our oars in and lay quiet.

SMITH: Drifted on your oars?

PITMAN: We may have drifted. We just lay there doing nothing.

SMITH: How many cries were there? Was it a chorus, or was it –

PITMAN: I would rather you did not speak about that … I can not very well describe it. I would rather you did not speak of it … There was a continual moan for about an hour.

SMITH: Did this anguish or those cries of distress die away?

PITMAN: Yes; they died away gradually.

A Night to Remember

WALTER LORD

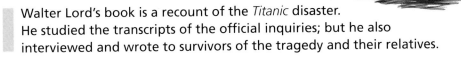

> Walter Lord's book is a recount of the *Titanic* disaster.
> He studied the transcripts of the official inquiries; but he also
> interviewed and wrote to survivors of the tragedy and their relatives.

Third Officer Herbert Pitman in Lifeboat No. 5 also heard the cries. He turned the boat around and shouted 'Now, men, we will pull towards the wreck!'

'Appeal to the officer not to go back,' a lady begged Steward Etches as he tugged at his oar. 'Why should we lose all our lives in a useless attempt to save others?'

Other women protested too. Pitman was torn by the dilemma. Finally he told his men to lay on their oars. For the next hour No. 5 – forty people in a boat that could hold sixty-five – heaved gently in the calm Atlantic swell, while its passengers listened to the swimmers three hundred yards away.

❖

In No.1, Fireman Charles Hendrickson sang out 'It's up to us to go back and pick up anyone in the water.'

Nobody answered. Lookout George Symons, in charge of the boat, made no move. Then, when the suggestion came again, Sir Cosmo Duff Gordon announced he didn't think they should try it; it would be too dangerous; the boat would be swamped. With that, the subject was dropped. No.1 – twelve people in a boat made for forty – rowed on in the dark.

In boat after boat the story was the same: a timid suggestion, a stronger refusal, nothing done. Of 1500 people who went down on the *Titanic*, only thirteen were picked up by the eighteen boats that hovered nearby.

❖

As the cries died away, the night became surprisingly peaceful. The *Titanic*, the agonizing suspense, was gone. The shock of what had happened, the realization that close friends were lost forever had not sunk in. A curiously tranquil feeling came over many of those in the boats.

❖

In boat No.4, Miss Jean Gertrude Hippach watched the shooting stars – she had never seen so many. She recalled a legend that every time there's a shooting star, someone dies.

Fried Eggs

FROM THE *BOOK OF HOUSEHOLD MANAGEMENT* BY MRS BEETON

INGREDIENTS.–4 eggs, ¼lb. of lard, butter or clarified dripping.

Mode.–Place a delicately-clean frying-pan over a gentle fire; put in the fat, and allow it to come to the boiling-point. Break the eggs into cups, slip them into the boiling fat, and let them remain until the whites are delicately set; and, whilst they are frying, ladle a little of the fat over them. Take them up with a slice, drain them for a minute from their greasy moisture, trim them neatly, and serve on slices of fried bacon or ham; or the eggs may be placed in the middle of the dish, with the bacon put round as a garnish.

Time.–2 to 3 minutes. *Average cost,* 1d each; 2d when scarce. *Sufficient* for 2 persons. *Seasonable* at any time.

VENERATION FOR EGGS.–Many of the most learned philosophers held eggs in a kind of respect, approaching to veneration, because they saw in them the emblem of the world and the four elements. The shell, they said, represented the earth; the white, water; the yolk, fire; and air was found under the shell at one end of the egg.

 There is more about eggs on page 54.

Chips

FROM *REAL FOOD* BY NIGEL SLATER

What I want of a chip depends on my mood. A rustling pile of thin *frites* with a rare steak; a parcel of slightly soggy thick-cut chips soaked in rough vinegar on the way home; or something in between – crisp and thick and fluffy inside – for pigging out at home with hot chilli sauce or a pot of garlicky mayonnaise as a 'chip dip'.

Enough for 2
4 large, floury potatoes
2 litres melted dripping or lard or sunflower oil for deep frying

Peel the potatoes and cut them into long, thick slices, about as long and thick as your fingers. Unless you have very big hands, in which case you should aim for about 1cm in width. Leave them in cold water to stop them sticking together.

Put the fat or oil to heat in a deep pan over a low flame. Bring it slowly up to 150°C. If you don't have a kitchen thermometer, you can check by adding a chip to the oil – if it sinks, then the oil is not hot enough. If it floats in a mass of bubbles, the temperature is right. Drain the chips and dry them on a clean tea towel, then put them in a frying basket and lower them gently into the fat. They will crackle and bubble alarmingly. Let them fry for about five minutes, until they are soft but still pale. Lift out and drain. Bring the oil up to 185°C. Be very careful at this point – the fat is very dangerous (you know this, but I just want to remind you). Return the chips to the fat for three to four minutes, shaking the basket now and again to help them brown evenly.

When they are golden brown and crisp, drain briefly on kitchen paper. Salt them enthusiastically and please don't forget to turn off the fat.

Some of the Rules of Hockey

ADAPTED FROM *RULES OF HOCKEY 1996* ISSUED BY THE
HOCKEY RULES BOARD

1 The field of play

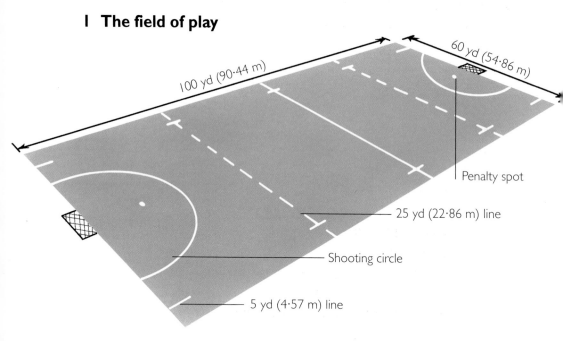

100 yd (90·44 m)

60 yd (54·86 m)

Penalty spot

25 yd (22·86 m) line

Shooting circle

5 yd (4·57 m) line

2 Teams

A game shall be played between 2 teams of not more than
16 players each, but not more than 11 players of each team
shall be on the field at the same time. Each team is permitted to
substitute from the maximum of 16 players.

3 Duration of play

a) A game shall consist of two periods of 35 minutes each.
b) There shall be an interval of 5 to 10 minutes at half time.
   Teams change ends for the second half.

4 Scoring a goal

a) A goal may be scored only by a player who is inside the shooting circle when he or she strikes the ball.

b) The ball must pass completely over the goal line and under the crossbar.

5 Conduct of play

Unless played with consideration for others, hockey can be a dangerous game.

Players must not:

- play the ball with the back of the stick
- play the ball above shoulder height with any part of the stick
- lift their sticks over the heads of players
- play the ball dangerously or in such a way as to be likely to lead to dangerous play
- hit, kick, shove, charge, trip another player or handle their stick or clothing
- throw any object onto the field, at the ball, at another player, or at an umpire.

Harry Potter and the Philosopher's Stone

J. K. ROWLING

Harry Potter, a new pupil at Hogwarts School of Witchcraft and Wizardry, is being taught the rules of a game called Quidditch. The aim of the game is to get a Quaffle through one of six hoops that are at the top of tall poles. The players are on flying broomsticks.

'Right,' said Wood. 'Now, Quidditch is easy enough to understand, even if it's not too easy to play. There are seven players on each side. Three of them are called Chasers.'

'Three Chasers,' Harry repeated, as Wood took out a bright-red ball about the size of a football.

'This ball's called the Quaffle,' said Wood. 'The Chasers throw the Quaffle to each other and try and get it through one of the hoops to score a goal. Ten points every time the Quaffle goes through one of the hoops. Follow me?'

'The Chasers throw the Quaffle and put it through the hoops to score,' Harry recited. 'So – that's sort of like basketball on broomsticks with six hoops, isn't it?'

'What's basketball?' said Wood curiously.

'Never mind,' said Harry quickly.

'Now, there's another player on each side who's called the Keeper – I'm Keeper for Gryffindor. I have to fly around our hoops and stop the other team from scoring.'

'Three Chasers, one Keeper,' said Harry, who was determined to remember it all. 'And they play with the Quaffle. OK, got that. So what are they for?' He pointed at the three balls left inside the box.

'I'll show you now,' said Wood. 'Take this.'

He handed Harry a small club, a bit like a rounders bat.

'I'm going to show you what the Bludgers do,' Wood said. 'These two are the Bludgers.'

He showed Harry two identical balls, jet black and slightly smaller than the red Quaffle. Harry noticed that they seemed to be straining to escape the straps holding them inside the box.

'Stand back,' Wood warned Harry. He bent down and freed one of the Bludgers.

At once, the black ball rose high in the air and then pelted straight at Harry's face. Harry swung at it with the bat to stop it breaking his nose and sent it zigzagging away into the air – it zoomed around their heads and then shot at Wood, who dived on top of it and managed to pin it to the ground.

'See?' Wood panted, forcing the struggling Bludger back into the crate and strapping it down safely. 'The Bludgers rocket around trying to knock players off their brooms. That's why you have two Beaters on each team – the Weasley twins are ours – it's their job to protect their side from the Bludgers and try and knock them towards the other team. So – think you've got all that?'

'Three Chasers try and score with the Quaffle; the Keeper guards the goal posts; the Beaters keep the Bludgers away from their team,' Harry reeled off.

'Very good,' said Wood.

'Er – have the Bludgers ever killed anyone?' Harry asked, hoping he sounded offhand.

'Never at Hogwarts. We've had a couple of broken jaws but nothing worse than that. Now, the last member of the team is the Seeker. That's you. And you don't have to worry about the Quaffle or the Bludgers –'

'– unless they crack my head open.'

'Don't worry, the Weasleys are more than a match for the Bludgers – I mean, they're like a pair of human Bludgers themselves.'

Wood reached into the crate and took out the fourth and last ball. Compared with the Quaffle and the Bludgers, it was tiny, about the size of a large walnut. It was bright gold and had little fluttering silver wings.

'*This*,' said Wood, 'is the Golden Snitch, and it's the most important ball of the lot. It's very hard to catch because it's so fast and difficult to see. It's the Seeker's job to catch it. You've got to weave in and out of the Chasers, Beaters, Bludgers and Quaffle to get it before the other team's Seeker, because whichever Seeker catches the Snitch wins his team an extra hundred and fifty points, so they nearly always win. That's why Seekers get fouled so much. A game of Quidditch only ends when the Snitch is caught, so it can go on for ages – I think the record is three months, they had to keep bringing on substitutes so the players could get some sleep.

'Well, that's it – any questions?'

Harry shook his head. He understood what he had to do all right, it was doing it that was going to be the problem.

The Torch

JILL PATON WALSH

In a strange future world, a group of children have become guardians of a sacred torch. One of them, Cal, is the book's narrator. Their travels have brought them to a ruined city in a desert, where tribes have gathered to compete in games.

'This can't be a race,' said Philip, looking round. 'What sort of event is it?'

'The first day we compete for story-telling, ' replied the Twaag. Each tribe puts its best story forward. Second and third day, races. Then we must disperse.'

'Why do you come so far to such a ruined place anyway?' I asked him.

'Long ago this was the capital city of all the desert tribes, of all the blue peoples,' he said. 'The King ruled in splendour. Then the river ran dry, and the wells were sluggish. Now there is water for only three days in the year. We can dwell in our own city for only so long ...'

'What made the wells dry up?' asked Peri.

'If I knew that ... ' said the Twaag expressively. 'Come, I show you the story-tellers ...'

He told us at each booth the name of the tribe, the name of the famous teller who would try to win the crown, the number of people in the tribe, and the name of their patch of desert. Some he praised for silversmithing, some for carpet-making, some as desert guides ... all this I forgot almost as soon as it was told me. One tribe he called

Hassides, and blamed them for cruelty. The taking and trading of slaves was their special craft, he said. And right at the far end of the stadium we came upon an old man, sitting in a story-teller's booth, with nobody round him. The rush mats for his people were spread out ready, and not a single soul had chosen to sit down.

'Is this man very bad at it?' asked Philip.

'Good – bad, nobody know, makes no difference,' said the Twaag. 'This man very sad. His people all die out. He the last man left who speaks his language … he know it all by heart, all the history of his tribe from the first time they came to the desert … and no one left to understand him.'

'How can they judge his story?' asked Cassie.

'Not try. King send judges to listen to all the other story-tellers. No judges for him.'

'And he doesn't mind?' I asked.

'Perhaps he not know. He been blind many years. Nobody tell him judges not listening. You come now and sit with Twaag …'

'No,' said Cassie. 'Thank you, but we will sit here.'

The Twaag laughed. 'You not understand anything. He not tell in English like all the others. Go on very very long time!'

But Cassie had already sat down, cross-legged, on the matting. I planted the torch upright in the sand, and sat down beside her. A great gong sounded, and a hush fell in the stadium. The old man began to intone, uttering strange sounds, and rocking himself gently as he spoke.

He spoke at first very low, an inaudible mutter, as though speaking to the deaf; and we clapped softly, and called to him, and saw his blank face turn to us with an expression of amazement, and heard his voice lift and ring out strongly in a rhythmical, joyful flow.

And the strange thing was that we did in a way understand. In the long incantation we heard the sound of battles, the length of journeys, we heard the pain and despair, and sudden upsurges of triumph and joy. I heard the aching voice longing for times past, and it put into my mind the flowing waters of the river below the

marble fields, the little white villages and red fields of home, and my mother's voice, crossed with love and complaint, droning on at me when the goats needed milking and water fetching and meal grinding, and I had been running among the poppies, and being a naughty child … In a while the urchin nestled up to me and put his thumb in his mouth, so that I thought he was falling asleep, but when I looked down at him I saw his eyes wide open. Cassie sat hugging her knees, her dark hair screening her face from view, and beyond her Peri lay sprawled, his head propped on one hand, but he too was wide awake. Even Philip, who couldn't sit still for long anywhere, paced up and down close by us and kept his eyes on the story-teller. I wanted Dio to be with us. I missed him.

The voice went on and on. We heard the distant applause as the other stories finished. The sun descended, and a honey-coloured light glowed over us. Then as the sand of the desert glowed rose pink, rose red, and the sky deepened from lilac to indigo, and we began to see the stars faint but strengthening above us, we realized we were no longer alone. Now that all the other performances had finished, curiosity had brought others to join us. A wide crowd had settled down quietly behind us, so that as the story-teller recounted how his people had died out one by one – or so I guessed from the sound – his hearers one by one increased. At last the King came too, and with him the crowd of judges. Then in the dusk there was a perfume. A heavy and delectable scent, like overblown roses, like the balsam pines of the mountains. It was all around us, so that at first I did not realize it was coming from the torch. But the King and all his people saw what happened. As the long story finished the torch leapt into life. No one was touching it; alone it fired up, with a rainbow of coloured flame and a fragrance like incense.

Cassie turned on me, in the lovely glow, a face full of joy. The King advanced, and set a victor's crown of woven red and silver on the old man's head, and the tribes whooped and called and clapped. ■

Two Men and a Bear

AESOP

Two men went on a journey which took them through wild country. As they were walking through a place of rocks and trees they saw a big bear coming towards them. One man fled in terror; he climbed a tree to escape from the bear. He was too scared to help the second man, who was left to face the bear alone.

The second man remembered something he'd been told: that bears won't touch anything they find which is already dead. So he lay down on the ground and pretended to be dead. The bear stalked up to the man on the ground and studied him; it put its nose close to the man's face and sniffed carefully; then it walked away.

When the bear was at a safe distance, the first man climbed down from the tree. 'From where I was,' he said, 'it looked as if that bear was whispering to you!'

The second man stood up. 'It was,' he said.

'Really?' said the first man. 'What did it say?'

'It told me that it is safer to travel alone than to travel with a coward,' said the second man. And he went on his way, alone.

51

To Find a Son and Heir

A Story from Zimbabwe

Raymond Wilson

A wrinkled father, more like a tortoise than
(what in fact he was) a rich old man,
sent word that his twin sons should come to the bed
on which he'd shortly die, and said:
'My sons, since you are twins, I've set a test
to settle which of you had best
inherit my great fortune. Here's ten pounds
each. Now then, I've built in the grounds
two empty rooms, identical in size,
and whichever of you is wise
enough to fill his room chock-full, yet still
have change out of the ten pounds, will
be heir to all I have.' Now apprehensive
of each other, the twins grew pensive
and sloped off to the dark forest's glades where
they pondered how they should prepare
themselves for the next day's trial. Their neighbours,
taking a holiday from their labours,
crowded about the two rooms, squinnying through
each slit, crack, hole in order to
see which of the twins would come up with the answer.
The first (hard-headed and no romancer)
drives up with a huge lorryful of sacks,
crates, cartons, boxes, which he stacks
in every nook and cranny, only to discover
that there are yawning gaps all over

and not the ghost of a hope of plugging any
of them with his remaining penny.
All eyes now turn towards the second son,
a dreamy youth, who hasn't done
a blind bit (so it seems) to get things ready,
but keeps his cool amid the heady
jeers of the crowd. Entering the empty room,
he gropes through the thronging shadow's gloom
to its still heart. There, placing it upright,
he sets a penny candle alight,
whose beams spread out in a golden dawn
to fill, flood and scour like a sun reborn
the room's small universe … The crowd, grown quiet,
begin to understand and riot,
clapping and cheering as, shoulder high, they bear
to the sick father his true son and heir. ▪

The Egg Cracks

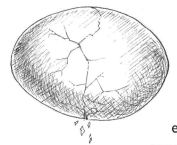

Before anything began, before time began, there was only a great chaos; and this chaos had the shape of a vast egg. Yin and Yang were inside this egg, and Yin and Yang are the two mighty, opposing energies that make up everything in the universe.

The struggle between these two great forces at last split the egg apart. The light, bright elements – the Yang elements – rose up and formed the sky. The dark, heavy elements – the Yin elements – sank down and formed the earth. And between these two, between the earth and the sky, stood the first being: his name was P'an-ku.

Little by little and day by day, for eighteen thousand years, the sky and the earth grew further apart. P'an-ku also grew, so that he always filled the space between the earth and the sky and kept them apart.

P'an-ku the giant was covered in fur. He had two horns, like a bull, and two tusks, like an elephant. If he grew angry, storms raged through the world. If he was happy, the weather was at peace with itself.

For all those long centuries, while the world was taking shape, P'an-ku used his great strength to keep the earth and the sky apart. At last he was exhausted, and he died. P'an-ku's body broke into pieces. His flesh became the land, and his head and limbs became the mountains. His breath became the wind, and his hair the plants and trees. His eyes became the sun and the moon.

And the fleas that lived on P'an-ku's body became mankind.

Yin and Yang: the opposites that make things whole
The ancient Chinese believed that everything that exists combines the two opposite forces, Yin and Yang. Yin is feminine, cool, dark and heavy; Yang is masculine, warm, bright and light. Earth and water are Yin; fire and air are Yang. Everything depends upon Yin and Yang being in the proper balance.

 There is more about eggs on page 40, and more about myths on page 12.

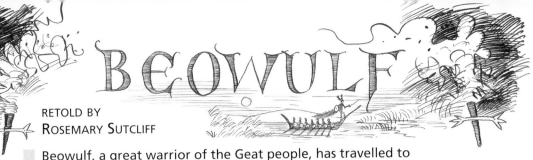

BEOWULF

RETOLD BY
ROSEMARY SUTCLIFF

Beowulf, a great warrior of the Geat people, has travelled to
Denmark, where people are being killed by a monster called Grendel.
Beowulf and his warriors are sleeping in the king's hall, Heorot.

I n the darkest hour of the spring night Grendel came to
Heorot as he had come so many times before, up from his
lair and over the high moors, through the mists that seemed
to travel with him under the pale moon; Grendel, the Night-
Stalker, the Death-Shadow. He came to the foreporch and
snuffed about it, and smelled the man-smell, and
found that the door which had
stood unlatched for him so long
was barred and bolted.
Snarling in rage that any
man should dare attempt
to keep him out, he set
the flat of his talon-tipped
hands against the timbers
and burst them in.

Dark as it was, the hall
seemed to fill with a
monstrous shadow at his
coming; a shadow in which
Beowulf, half springing up,
then holding himself in
frozen stillness, could make
out no shape nor clear

outline save two eyes filled with a wavering greenish flame.

The ghastly corpse-light of his own eyes showed Grendel the shapes of men as it seemed sleeping, and he did not notice among them one who leaned up on his elbow. Laughing in his throat, he reached out and grabbed young Hondscio who lay nearest to him, and almost before his victim had time to cry out, tore him limb from limb and drank the warm blood. Then, while the young warrior's dying shriek still hung upon the air, he reached for another. But this time his hand was met and seized in a grasp such as he had never felt before; a grasp that had in it the strength of thirty men. And for the first time he who had brought fear to so many caught the taste of it himself, knowing that at last he had met his match and maybe his master.

Beowulf leapt from the sleeping-bench and grappled him in the darkness; and terror broke over Grendel in full force, the terror of a wild animal trapped; so that he thought no more of his hunting but only breaking the terrible hold upon his arm and flying back into the night and the wilderness, and he howled and bellowed as he struggled for his freedom. Beowulf set his teeth and summoned all his strength and tightened his grip until the sinews cracked; and locked together they reeled and staggered up and down the great hall. Trestles and sleeping-benches went over with crash on crash as they strained this way and that, trampling even through the last red embers of the dying fire; and the very walls seemed to groan and shudder as though the stout timbers would burst apart. And all the while Grendel snarled and shrieked and Beowulf fought in silence save  for his gasping breaths.

Outside, the Danes listened in horror to the turmoil that seemed as though it must split Heorot asunder; and within, the Geats had sprung from their sleeping-benches sword in hand, forgetful of their powerlessness against the Troll-kind, but in the dark, lit only by stray gleams of bale-fire from the monster's eyes, they dared not strike for fear of slaying their leader, and when one or other of them did contrive to get in a blow, the sword blade glanced off Grendel's charmed hide as though he were sheathed in dragon scales.

At last, when the hall was wrecked to the walls, the Night-Stalker gathered himself for one last despairing effort to break free. Beowulf's hold was as fierce as ever; yet none the less the two figures burst apart – and Grendel with a frightful shriek staggered to the door-way and through it, and fled wailing into the night, leaving his arm and shoulder torn from the roots in the hero's still unbroken grasp.

 There is more about monsters on pages 16, 19 and 58, and more about legendary heroes on pages 60, 98 and 99.

Things that go Bump in the Night

WILBUR G. HOWCROFT

If you see the Possawassa
Skulking in the night,
Turn out the lights, lock fast the doors
And close the windows tight.

Stuff cinnamon inside your ears,
Stand upon your head,
Poke out your tongue, cross both your eyes –
Pretend that you are dead.

If some night the Collywhicker
Knocks upon your door,
Rub peanut butter in your hair
And eat an onion raw.

Hang lots of garlic round your neck,
Paint both your kneecaps blue,
Then softly croon that old refrain –
'Sweet Alice, Where She To?'

If the Tootsie Tumbaroo calls
When you're having tea,
Start crowing like a crocodile
And set the Budgie free.

Tie yellow ribbons to your toes,
Give three rousing cheers,
Remove your hat and quickly place
Your head between your ears.

If the fearsome Malapunkas
Come around in herds
Spray smelling salts beneath the arms
Of all your humming birds.

Place baited mouse traps in the bath,
Pour honey in your socks,
Then slyly raise a window up
And pepper them with rocks.

If the dreaded Wooza Doofla
Tries to come inside,
Tuck both your feet beneath your chin
Then scamper off and hide.

Should he fail to go off smartly,
Call out loud and clear;

'You'd better find another house,
There's no one living here!'

There is more about monsters
on pages 16, 19 and 55.

King Arthur

After the death of Uther Pendragon, it is not clear who should become King of England. Several lords have their eye on the throne, and there is danger of war between them. The Archbishop of Canterbury summons all the noblemen and knights of England to come to London to pray for a sign as to who should be King.

The Historie of King Arthur

SIR THOMAS MALORY, 1469

And when matins and the first masse was done, there was seene in the churchyard, against the hie altar, a great stone foure square, like to a marble stone, and in the midest thereof was an anvile of steele, a foote of height, and therein stooke a faire sword naked by the point, and letters of gold were written about the sword that said thus: WHO SO PULLETH OUT THIS SWORD OF THIS STONE AND ANVILE, IS RIGHTWISE KING BORNE OF ENGLAND. Then the people marvailed and told it to the archbishop.

"I commaund you," said the archbishop, "that you keepe you within your church, and pray unto God stil that no man touch the sword til the hie mas be al done." So when al the masses were don, al the lords went for to behold the stone and the sword. And when they saw the scripture, some assaied, such as would have been king. But none might stir the sword nor move it.

"He is not yet here," said the archbishop, "that shal achieve the sword, but doubt not God will make him knowne."

keepe you: stay   *assaied*: tried (to pull out the sword)   *achieve*: win, or take

60

Four hundred years later, another writer continues the story.

The Legends of King Arthur and his Knights

S~IR~ J~AMES~ K~NOWLES~, **1862**

Now, at the New Year's Eve a great tournament was to be held in London, which the archbishop had devised to keep together lords and commons, lest they should grow estranged in the troublous and unsettled times. To the which tournament there came with many other knights, Sir Ector, Arthur's foster-father, who had great possessions near to London; and with him came his son, Sir Key, but recently made knight, to take his part in the jousting, and young Arthur also to witness all the sports and fighting.

commons: the common people   *possessions*: land and property

The Sword in the Stone

T. H. WHITE, 1938

On the first day of the tournament, Sir Kay managed to get them on the way to the lists at least an hour before the jousts could possibly begin. He had lain awake all night, imagining how he was going to beat the best barons in England, and he had not been able to eat his breakfast. Now he rode at the front of the cavalcade, with pale cheeks, and Wart wished there was something he could do to calm him down.

For country people who only knew the dismantled tilting ground of Sir Ector's castle, the scene which now met their eyes was really ravishing. It was a huge green pit in the earth, about as big as the arena at a football match. It lay about ten feet lower than the surrounding country, with sloping banks, and all the snow had been swept off it. It had been kept warm with straw, which had been cleared off that morning, and now all the close-mown grass sparkled green in the white landscape. Round the arena there was a world of colour so dazzling and moving and twinkling as to make you blink your eyes. The wooden grandstands were painted in scarlet and white. The silk pavilions of famous people, pitched on every side, were azure and green and saffron and chequered. The pennons and pennoncells which floated everywhere in the sharp wind were flapping with every colour of the rainbow, as they strained and slapped at their flagpoles, and the barrier down the middle of the arena itself was done in chessboard squares of black and white. Most of the combatants and their friends had not yet arrived, but you could see from those few who had arrived how

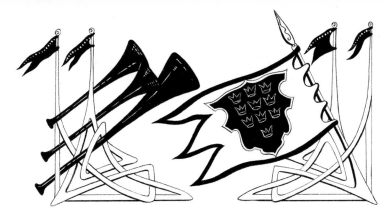

the very people would turn the scene into a bank of flowers, and how the armour would flash, and the scalloped sleeves of the heralds jig in the wind, as they raised their brazen trumpets to their lips to shake the fleecy clouds of winter with joyances and fanfares.

"Good heavens!" cried Sir Kay. "I have left my sword at home."

"Can't joust without a sword," said Sir Grummore. "Quite irregular."

"Better go and fetch it," said Sir Ector. "You have time."

"My squire will do," said Sir Kay. "What a damned mistake to make. Here, squire, ride hard back to the inn and fetch my sword. You shall have a shilling if you fetch it in time."

The Wart went as pale as Sir Kay was, and looked as if he were going to strike him. Then he said, "It shall be done, Master," and turned his stupid little ambling palfrey against the stream of newcomers. He began to push his way towards their hostelry as best he might.

"To offer me money!" cried the Wart to himself. "To look down at this beastly little donkey-affair off his great charger and call me Squire! Oh, Merlyn, give me patience with the brute, and stop me from throwing his filthy shilling in his face."

When he got to the inn it was closed. ▪

lists: the enclosed space where a tournament is held   *tilting ground*: practice ground for jousting   *joyances*: joyful sounds   *palfrey*: a small horse ridden by ladies

In this version written at the end of the twentieth century, Arthur finally pulls the sword out. But first he has to go back to the inn to fetch the one that Kay should be using …

King Arthur and the Round Table

GERALDINE McCAUGHREAN, 1996

He beat on the door, but nobody came. The landlady had gone out! He saw an open upper window, and climbed on to a cart, but he was not tall enough to reach the sill. He thought of buying a sword: he had no money. He thought of borrowing one, but on tournament day? Who would part with their weapon? He thought of stealing one, but that would have shamed both him and Kay.

On the precinct of Westminster Abbey-church, he prayed a fervent prayer: "Oh God! Please give me a sword!"

And there it was. A big slab of rock, such as builders might abandon, lay in the long grass. On top of it was a blacksmith's anvil. And wedged into the anvil – a sword!

Somewhere a trumpet fanfare blew. Another few moments and Kay would be disqualified, disgraced, for want of a sword. Arthur leapt on to the stone, braced his knees against the anvil and gripped the swordhilt. "I'll fetch it back, I promise!" he said, aloud, thinking this might be a gravestone of some dead knight. The sword slipped out easily.

A woman passer-by stopped and stared, open-mouthed. "A loan, that's all," called Arthur apologetically, and ran. The passer-by stopped a man. Behind him Arthur could hear their shocked voices:

"Did you see?"

"That boy just …"

Arthur tore back along the street, the sword tucked under his arm for fear of running into someone. He was just in time. Another fanfare sounded, as he thrust the sword into his brother's hands.

Kay staggered. "This isn't mine."

"No. The lodgings … I'm sorry … found it." Arthur was too out of breath to explain.

Kay slid the sword home into his saddle-sheath. The sheath's stitching was instantly sliced through and the bare sword fell to the ground. Kay picked it up. Arthur bit his lip.

The woman who had seen Arthur take the sword came pushing through the crowds. The man was close behind. "That boy," she said, pointing, "He just took …"

"Oh pig's-feathers," muttered Arthur and tried to melt out of sight.

But the crowd grew more and more noisy, more and more excitable. "The boy pulled the sword out of the anvil! I tell you he did!"

"Don't be ridiculous!"

"I know what I saw!"

The stewards and heralds on the field of tourney noticed the disturbance and came asking questions. They found Kay surrounded by peasants and merchants and housewives, sullying his armour with their dirty fingers and saying, "The boy pulled the sword out of the anvil!"

"This knight?"

Kay's eyes met his father's. He said nothing.

"No! T'other one. The boy. There!"

There was no escaping the huge circle of people which pressed in on Kay, Sir Ector, Arthur and the borrowed sword.

Sir Ector laid both hands on Arthur's shoulders. "Tell me, Arthur. Where did you find the sword?"

"I'm sorry. I pulled it out of some anvil in a stone beside the Abbey. I meant to take it back after Kay … I never knew it would cause such a …" The crowd gave such a gasp that he faltered. The knights off the tourney field seemed unreasonably angry.

"Absurd."

"It's a lie."

"A fraud."

The jostling crowds began moving back through the streets, the tournament forgotten. Kay and Arthur and Sir Ector were swept along by it. Kay still had hold of the borrowed sword.

"What have I done, father?" Arthur pleaded to know.

"Did you read the words carved on the stone, boy?" said Sir Ector. He seemed oddly calm.

"Words? No. The grass was long ..."

In the Abbey precinct, the press of people round about the stone and anvil soon trod flat the long grass. Words carved around the base were uncovered one by one:

WHO PULLS ... THIS ANVIL ... OF ENGL ...

A knight snatched the sword out of Kay's hand and staggered a little – "a boy couldn't lift this" – as he pushed the blade back into the slot in the anvil. "Now show us," he sneered.

Arthur did not move. So Kay took hold of the swordhilt and pulled till his face turned red. The sword did not budge.

An older, much grander knight shouldered him out of the way and hauled on the sword till his face turned purple and he griped at his stomach. But the sword did not budge. Arthur felt Sir Ector's hand on his shoulder, pushing him forward. He stepped up on to the rock and pulled out the sword as easily as a knife out of butter. ▪

tourney: tournament   *sullying*: soiling

There is more about legendary heroes on pages 55, 98 and 99.

From a Railway Carriage

ROBERT LOUIS STEVENSON

Faster than fairies, faster than witches,
Bridges and houses, hedges and ditches;
And charging along like troops in a battle,
All through the meadows the horses and cattle:
All the sights of the hill and the plain
Fly as thick as driving rain;
And ever again, in the wink of an eye,
Painted stations whistle by.

Here is a child who clambers and scrambles,
All by himself and gathering brambles;
Here is a tramp who stands and gazes;
And there is a green for stringing the daisies!
Here is a cart run away in the road
Lumping along with man and load;
And here is a mill, and there is a river:
Each a glimpse and gone for ever!

The Fox

A hungry fox went out one night –
He begged the moon to give him light
For he had many miles to trot that night
Before he could reach 'is dinno,
Dinno, dinno. Before he could reach 'is dinno.

Soon he reached the farmer's yard;
The ducks and geese declared it hard;
Their nerves were shaken and rest was marred
By a visit by Mister Foxo,
Foxo, Foxo. A visit by Mister Foxo.

He grabbed the black duck by the neck
And flung him all across his back;
The black duck cried out, "Quack, quack, quack,"
And his heels hung dangling downo,
Downo, downo. And his heels hung dangling downo.

Old Lady Slipper-slopper jumped out of bed,
Hoist up the window and thrust out her head,
Crying, "John, John, John, the black duck's gone;
The fox is off to his dinno."
Dinno, dinno. The fox is off to his dinno.

John ran up on the hill
And blew a blast both loud and shrill.
Said the fox, "That's pretty music still
I would rather be off to my dinno."
Dinno, dinno. I would rather be off to my dinno.

Master fox trotted off to his den,
To his dear little foxes, eight, nine, ten;
Showing the luck of a good fat duck
And his legs hang dangling downo,
Down, downo. And his legs hang dangling downo.

Master fox and his hungry wife
Ate very well without fork and knife;
They never had a better meal in all their life
And the little ones slicked the boneso,
Boneso, boneso. And the little ones slicked the boneso.

The Spider and the Fly

MARY HOWITT

'Will you walk into my parlour?' said the Spider to the Fly,
''Tis the prettiest little parlour that ever you did spy;
The way into my parlour is up a winding stair,
And I have many curious things to show when you are there.'
'Oh no, no,' said the little Fly, 'to ask me is in vain,
For who goes up your winding stair can ne'er come down again.'

'I'm sure you must be weary, dear, with soaring up so high;
Will you rest upon my little bed?' said the Spider to the Fly.
'There are pretty curtains drawn around, the sheets are fine and thin;
And if you like to rest awhile, I'll snugly tuck you in!'
'Oh no, no,' said the little Fly, 'for I've often heard it said
They never, never wake again, who sleep upon your bed!'

Said the cunning Spider to the Fly, 'Dear friend, what can I do,
To prove the warm affection I've always felt for you?
I have within my pantry good store of all that's nice;
I'm sure you're very welcome – will you please to take a slice?'
'Oh no, no,' said the Fly, 'kind sir, that cannot be,
I've heard what's in your pantry, and I do not wish to see.'

'Sweet creature,' said the Spider, 'you're witty and you're wise;
How handsome are your gauzy wings, how brilliant are your eyes!
I have a little looking-glass upon my parlour shelf,
If you'll step in a moment, dear, you shall behold yourself.'
'I thank you, gentle sir,' she said, 'for what you're pleased to say,
And bidding you good morning now, I'll call another day.'

The Spider turned him round about, and went into his den,
For well he knew the silly Fly would soon come back again;
So he wove a subtle web, in a little corner sly,
And set his table ready, to dine upon the Fly.
Then he came out to his door again, and merrily did sing:
'Come hither, hither, pretty Fly, with the pearl and silver wing;
Your robes are green and purple – there's a crest upon your head;
Your eyes are like the diamond bright, but mine are dull as lead.'

Alas, alas! how very soon this silly little Fly,
Hearing his wily, flattering words, came slowing flitting by;
With buzzing wings she hung aloft, then near and nearer drew,
Thinking only of her brilliant eyes, and green and purple hue;
Thinking only of her crested head – poor foolish thing! At last,
Up jumped the cunning Spider, and fiercely held her fast.
He dragged her up his winding stair, into his dismal den,
Within his little parlour – but she ne'er came out again!

 There is more about spiders on page 82.

Cool Cat

MIKE JUBB

Well I'm a cat with nine
And I'm in my prime
I'm a Casanova Cat
And I'm feline fine
I'm strolling down the street
In my white slipper feet
Yeh, all the little lady cats
Are looking for a treat
Because I got style
I got a naughty smile
I'm gonna cross this street
In just a little while
   to be with you
   to be with you
   to be with you
   to be with
You got grace
You got a lickable face
I'm gonna love ya and leave ya
And you'll never find a trace
Because I'm on my own
I like to be alone
I'm just a swingin', strollin'
Rollin' stone
But it's your lucky day
I'm gonna pass your way
I can spare a little lovin'
If you wanna stop and
   play with me
   play with me
   play with me
   play with
Meeow my
I got a twinkling eye

I'm gonna cross this street
So don't you be too shy
But what's this I see
Comin' straight at me
It's a crazy car driver
Tryin' to make me flee
So I look up slow
Just to let the man know
That I don't go any faster
Than I really wanna go.

X ! X ! X ! X ! X ! X ! X ! X ! X

Well I'm a cat with eight
I guess he couldn't wait
But I'm lookin' good
And I'm feline great!

The Private Life of the Otter

FROM *THE SHADOW OF*
EXTINCTION: EUROPE'S
THREATENED WILD ANIMALS
BY JEREMY MALLINSON

Habitat

Otters live beside lakes, rivers, streams, canals and marshes as well
as in coastal waters where they have been caught in crab and
lobster pots. They try to avoid polluted rivers and prefer stretches
where there is plenty of cover on the banks. They are sometimes
found far from water, but usually only when crossing a watershed
from one river system to another. In more mountainous areas they
have been observed up to 2800m; it has been suggested that they
move up to the headwaters when fish migrate there to spawn,
then come down to lower waters and the coast in the spring.

Behaviour

The otter is an expert swimmer and diver, but while on land its
action is a fast waddle. The legs are rather short, so the body is
kept near the ground. As the hindlegs are longer, the hind part of
the back appears curiously arched; nevertheless, otters can run
quite fast, but not as fast as a dog or a fox.

Otters can be active day and night, although they are usually
nocturnal for they are very shy and cautious. During the
daytime they lie up in burrows or holts. The holt is a natural
hole, or one the otter has dug for itself, in the bank of a river,
stream or lake. It has several passages and a roomy living
chamber above the level of the water, lined with dry grass and
the like, and provided with a ventilation shaft to ground level.
One entrance is always under water. Other entrances and exits

are recognizable by tracks and the remains of food.

With the possible exception of the badger, river otters are probably the most playful of the *Mustelidae*. They live alone or in families, but when together their acrobatics are wonderful to watch as they chase and wrestle each other in the water. They will use any convenient object as a toy – a log, for instance, as it rotates in the water, will keep them amused for a long time – and they will constantly dive for pebbles and try to bring them up to the surface. Some species engage in the year-round activity of sliding down mud and snow banks, and individuals of all ages participate.

Although silent for long periods, otters can make a variety of sounds, the best known being the shrill whistle which appears to serve as a means of communicating location. A long drawn-out moan probably denotes apprehension, while a rather high-pitched chortle is commonly used when pleased, and a hiss or high-pitched chatter when annoyed.

Diet

Fish forms the basic diet of European otters. But their food is very variable, depending on the locality and the abundance of the prey, so many other kinds of animal are eaten, and crustaceans form an important part of their diet. Among the food items that they have been recorded to eat are eels, trout, salmon, minnows, crayfish, crabs, newts, tadpoles, frogs, snails, earthworms, beetles, fresh-water shrimps and even aquatic birds. Various mammals are also eaten occasionally, especially rabbits and small rodents such as rats and water-voles; carrion is also taken.

 There is more about animals that live near water on page 24.

Dragons Around the World

DAVID PASSES

At one time or another, stories about dragons have been told in most countries of the world. As the pictures in this book show, not all dragons have four legs, clawed feet and wings. They come in many different shapes, colours and sizes. Some dragons are part of local folklore or a national legend. Others appear as isolated reports in monastic records or in early naturalists' notes. What follows is a selection of dragons from around the world.

The Amphisbaena (Africa)

This dragon had a head at each end and could move in either direction. While an Amphisbaena's eggs were hatching, she could keep one head awake at a time to watch over them. Today there is a South American limbless lizard that gives the impression of having two heads. When threatened, it raises its tail and moves backwards and forwards.

The Midgard Serpent (Scandinavia)

The Midgard Serpent of Scandinavian mythology was so long that it slept in the sea with its tail in its mouth, and its body encircled the world. According to the myth, Midgard will wake at the end of the world and be killed by Thor, god of war and thunder, who will also die in the struggle.

The O-Gon-Cho (Japan)

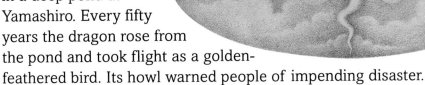

The O-Gon-Cho was a white dragon that lived in a deep pond at Yamashiro. Every fifty years the dragon rose from the pond and took flight as a golden-feathered bird. Its howl warned people of impending disaster.

The Piasa (North America)

The Algonquin Indians of North America worshipped a dragon with the face of a man and a tail so long that it passed over its body and head, and between its legs. An ancient 'life-sized' painting of the dragon once existed on Piasa Rock in Illinois, but it was unfortunately blown up by workers quarrying for stones. In the Algonquin language, piasa means 'man-eating bird'.

 There is more about dragons on pages 22, 23 and 102.

A London Evacuee sees his First Cow

BBC News
Quoted by Robert Westall, *Children of the Blitz*

The cow is a mammal. It has six sides, right, left, and upper and below. At the back is a tail, on which hangs a brush. With this it sends the flies away so they do not fall into the milk. The head is for the purpose of growing horns and so that the mouth can be somewhere. The horns are to butt with, and the mouth to moo with. Under the cow hangs the milk. It is arranged for milking. When people milk, the milk comes and there is never an end to the supply. How the cow does it I have not realized but it makes more and more. The cow has a fine sense of smell; one can smell it far away. This is the reason for the fresh air in the country.

The man cow is called an ox. It is not a mammal. The cow does not eat much but what it eats, it eats twice so that it gets enough. When it is hungry it moos and when it says nothing it is because all its inside is full up with grass. ▪

 There is more about evacuees on pages 10 and 14.

Tongue

Macmillan Encyclopedia

currency: pa'anga of 100 seniti. Area: 700 sq. km (270 sq. mi.). Population: (1987): 94,800. Capital and main port: Nuku'alofa

tongue A muscular organ situated in the floor of the mouth. The root of the tongue is attached by muscles to the U-shaped hyoid bone in the neck. The tongue is the main organ of taste; its surface is covered by minute projections (giving it a rough appearance) around which the taste buds are grouped, detecting sweet, sour, salt and bitter tastes. It also manipulates food during chewing and swallowing and helps in the articulation of speech. Furring of the tongue is a sympton of fever; a smooth and sore tongue may indicate anaemia.

Tong Zhi (*or* T'ung-chih; 1856–75) The title of Cai-chun (*or* Tsai-ch'un). Chinese emperor (1862–75); the son of Zi Xi, who acted as regent

Taste and Smell

FROM *THE DORLING KINDERSLEY SCIENCE ENCYCLOPEDIA*

Animals use the senses of taste and smell to detect chemicals. When you taste something, groups of cells on your tongue, called taste-buds, detect chemicals dissolved in your saliva. When you smell something, cells at the top of your nose detect chemicals dissolved in the moist lining of your nose. Taste-buds detect only what we describe as sweet, sour, salt and bitter. Flavours are combinations of these four, so they are much more varied. Taste is linked to the sense of smell, which is why it is hard to tell different foods apart if your nose is blocked.

Most taste-buds lie in tiny grooves in the surface of the tongue.

SMELL

Some animals use scents to send and receive messages. For example, dogs leave their scent to mark their territory, or to let other dogs know they are around. Dogs use their sense of smell to build up a 'picture' of the world around them.

TASTE

Different taste-buds on an animal's tongue detect different tastes, such as sweet or sour. An animal's sense of taste enables it to tell if something is good or bad to eat. Animals use this sense to choose food to eat, and to avoid eating something poisonous.

Blood, Bones and Body Bits

NICK ARNOLD

Terrible Tastes

To find out more about taste you've got to peer into your wet drooling mouth. Better take a look now before you chicken out!

Look closely at your tongue. Say Aghhhhhhhhh! Can you see those little bumps and lines? The little lines are crammed with 8,000 or so taste buds linked to the brain by nerves. Different buds handle sweet, sour, salty and bitter tastes.

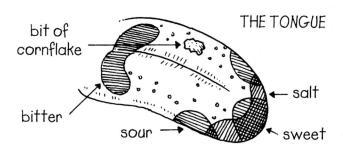

bit of cornflake

THE TONGUE

bitter

salt

sour

sweet

The really tasteless question is – why are you supposed to taste bitter things at all? I mean – how many bitter-tasting foods do you actually like enough to eat? Well, you're not actually meant to eat most of them – spitting them out would be a lot better for you. This is because most poisons taste bitter, so the bitter-sensitive taste buds are there to tell you that you're just about to eat some vile POISON.

The Silken Trap

How the spider produces thread

spinnerets

abdomen

Liquid silk is produced by special glands inside the spider's body. These glands almost completely fill the spider's abdomen. The silk comes out through tiny nozzles called *spinnerets*. Most spiders have three pairs of spinnerets, and they can be pointed in different directions when the spider is spinning. The liquid silk contains a substance called *fibroin*; when the spider draws the silk from its spinnerets the fibroin hardens and turns the liquid into a solid thread.

Spiders produce different kinds of thread. Sticky thread is used to catch prey. Dry thread is used for a number of purposes: to make cocoons, to build a nest or 'parlour' near the edge of the web, and to make a 'lookout platform' at the centre where the spider waits motionless for prey.

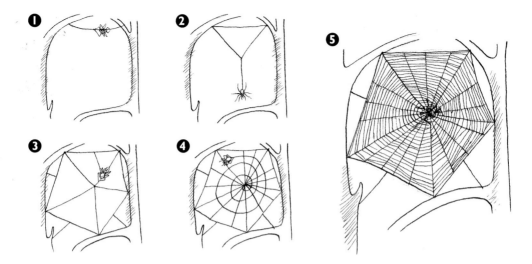

How a female garden spider constructs her web

The female garden spider first spins a thread which floats in the air until it reaches a solid object and sticks to it. This is her bridge-line [1]. Next, she strings a loose thread beneath the *bridge-line* and drops down from the middle of it to make a Y shape [2]. The fork in the Y will be the centre, or hub of the web. Then she builds the outer framework of the web and builds *radials* from the framework to the hub [3]. The spider now builds a spiral of dry thread from the hub outwards [4]. This spiral is only temporary; it holds the web together while she builds the sticky spiral which will trap her prey. She lays down this sticky spiral working from the outside of the web towards the hub, attaching it to each of the radials [5]. She eats the temporary dry spiral as she goes along it. (It contains valuable protein which she digests and recycles to make more silk.) She leaves the central part of the dry spiral, though: this will be the platform on which she sits to wait for her meal to come along. Spiders usually spin their webs at night, because it's safer: they are less likely to be seen by birds.

 There is more about spiders on page 70.

When Hitler Stole Pink Rabbit

Judith Kerr

This novel opens in Germany in 1933.

Chapter 1

Anna was walking home from school with Elsbeth, a girl in her class. A lot of snow had fallen in Berlin that winter. It did not melt, so the street cleaners had swept it to the edge of the pavement, and there it had lain for weeks in sad, greying heaps. Now, in February, the snow had turned into slush and there were puddles everywhere. Anna and Elsbeth skipped over them in their lace-up boots.

They both wore thick coats and woollen caps which kept their ears warm, and Anna had a muffler as well. She was nine but small for her age and the ends of the muffler hung down almost to her knees. It also covered up her mouth and nose, so the only parts of her that showed were her green eyes and a tuft of dark hair. She had been hurrying because she wanted to buy some crayons at the paper shop and it was nearly time for lunch. But now she was so out of breath that she was glad when Elsbeth stopped to look at a large red poster.

"It's another picture of that man," said Elsbeth. "My little sister saw one yesterday and thought it was Charlie Chaplin."

Anna looked at the staring eyes, the grim expression. She said, "It's not a bit like Charlie Chaplin except for the moustache."

They spelled out the name under the photograph.
Adolf Hitler.

"He wants everybody to vote for him in the elections and then he's going to stop the Jews," said Elsbeth. "Do you think he's going to stop Rachel Lowenstein?"

"Nobody can stop Rachel Lowenstein," said Anna. "She's form

captain. Perhaps he'll stop me. I'm Jewish too."

"You're not!"

"I am! My father was talking to us about it only last week. He said we were Jews and no matter what happened my brother and I must never forget it."

"But you don't go to a special church on Saturdays like Rachel Lowenstein."

"That's because we're not religious. We don't go to church at all."

"I wish my father wasn't religious," said Elsbeth. "We have to go every Sunday and I get cramp in my seat." She looked at Anna curiously. "I thought Jews were supposed to have bent noses, but your nose is quite ordinary. Has your brother got a bent nose?"

"No," said Anna. "The only person in our house with a bent nose is Bertha the maid, and hers only got like that because she broke it falling off a tram."

Elsbeth was getting annoyed. "Well then," she said, "if you look the same as everyone else and you don't go to a special church, how do you know you *are* Jewish? How can you be sure?"

There was a pause.

"I suppose…" said Anna, "I suppose it's because my mother and father are Jews, and I suppose their mothers and fathers were too. I never thought about it much until Papa started talking about it last week."

"Well, I think it's silly!" said Elsbeth. "It's silly about Adolf Hitler and people being Jews and everything!" She started to run and Anna followed her. ▪

ADOLF HITLER

The Cay

THEODORE TAYLOR

> The year is 1942. A young White boy, Phillip, and an old West Indian
> sailor, Timothy, have survived a German submarine attack on a ship
> bound for The United States. During the attack, Philip has been struck
> on the head and has lost his eyesight. After three days adrift on a raft,
> they land on a tiny, unnamed Caribbean island, or cay.

In the afternoon, Timothy said we'd make a rope.

On the north end of the island, tough vines, almost as large as a pencil, were laced over the sand. It took us several hours to tear out a big pile of them. Then Timothy began weaving a rope that would stretch all the way down the hill to the beach and fire pile.

The rope was for me. If he happened to be out on the reef, and I heard a plane, I could take a light from our campfire, follow the rope down, and touch off the big fire. The vine rope would also serve to get me safely down to the beach.

After we'd torn the vines out, and he was weaving the rope, he said, 'Young Bahss, you mus' begin to help wid d'udder wark.'

We were sitting up by the hut. I had my back to a palm and was thinking that back in Willemstad, at this moment, I'd probably be sitting in a classroom, three desks away from Henrik, listening to Herr Jonckheer talk about European history. I'd been tutored in Dutch the first year in Willemstad so I could attend the regular school. Now I could speak and understand it.

Willemstad: Phillip's home on the Dutch-owned island of Curacao
reeve: tie

My hands were tired from pulling the vines, and I just wanted to sit and think. I didn't want to work. I said 'Timothy, I'm blind. I can't see to work.'

I heard him cutting something with his sharp knife. He replied softly, 'D'han' is not blin'.'

Didn't the old man understand? To work, aside from pulling up vines or drawing something in the sand, you must be able to see.

Stubbornly, he said, 'Young bahss, we need sleepin' mats. You can make d'mats.'

I looked over in his direction. 'You do it,' I said.

He sighed back, saying, 'D'best matmaker in Charlotte Amalie, downg in Frenchtown, b'total blin'.'

'But he's a man, and he has to do that to make a living.'

'B'true,' Timothy said quietly.

But in a few minutes, he placed several lengths of palm fibre across my lap. He really was a black mule.

'D'palm mat is veree easy. Jus' ovah an' under …'

Becoming angry with him, I said, 'I tell you, I can't see.'

He paid no attention to me. 'Take dis han' hol' d'palm like

dis; den ovah an' under, like d'mahn in Frenchtown; den more palm.'

I could feel him standing there watching me as I tried to reeve the lengths, but I knew they weren't fitting together. He said, 'Like dis, I tell you,' and reached down to guide my hand. 'Ovah an' under …'

I tried again, but it didn't work. I stood up, threw the palm fibres at him, and screamed, 'You ugly black man! I won't do it! You're stupid, you can't even spell …'

Timothy's heavy hand struck my face sharply.

Stunned, I touched my face where he'd hit me. Then I turned away from where I thought he was. My cheek stung, but I wouldn't let him see me with tears in my eyes.

I heard him saying very gently, 'B'gettin' back to wark, my own self.'

I sat down again.

He began to sing that 'fungee and feesh' song in a low voice, and I could picture him sitting on the sand in front of the hut; that tangled grey hair, the ugly black face with the thick lips, those great horny hands winding the strands of vine.

The rope, I thought. It wasn't for him. It was for me.

After a while, I said, 'Timothy …'

He did not answer, but walked over to me, pressing more palm fronds into my hands. He murmured, ''Tis veree easy, ovah an' under …' Then he went back to singing about fungee and feesh.

Something happened to me that day on the cay. I'm not quite sure what it was even now, but I had begun to change.

I said to Timothy, 'I want to be your friend.'

He said softly, 'Young bahss, you 'ave always been my friend.'

I said, 'Can you call me Phillip instead of young boss?'

'Phill-eep,' he said warmly. ▪

Walkabout

JAMES VANCE MARSHALL

> Two White American children, Mary and her younger brother Peter, are the only survivors of a plane crash deep in the Australian desert. Cut off from their 'civilized' world of cars and supermarkets, they have no idea how to survive. They suddenly come face to face with a naked young Aborigine – a 'bush boy'.

The desert sun streamed down. The children stared and stared.

Mary had decided not to move. To move would be a sign of weakness. She remembered being told about the man who'd come face to face with a lion, and had stared it out, had caused it to slink discomforted away. That was what she'd do to the black boy; she'd stare at him until he felt the shame of his nakedness and slunk away. She thrust out her chin, and glared.

Peter had decided to take his cue from his sister. Clutching her hand he stood waiting: waiting for something to happen.

The Aboriginal was in no hurry. Time had little value to him. His next meal – the rock wallaby – was assured. Water was near. Tomorrow was also a day. For the moment he was content to examine these strange creatures at his leisure. Their clumsy, lumbering movements intrigued him, their lack of weapons indicated their harmlessness. His eyes moved slowly, methodically from one to another: examining them from head to foot. They were the first white people a member of his tribe had ever seen.

Mary, beginning to resent this scrutiny, intensified her glare. But the bush boy seemed in no way perturbed; his appraisal went methodically on.

After a while, the Aborigine loses interest and simply walks away.

'Hey, Mary!' Peter gasped. 'Come on. After him!'
He went crashing into the bush. Slowly, doubtfully, his sister followed.

'Hey, darkie!' Peter's reedy treble echoed down the valley. 'We wanna come too. Wait for us!'

'Hey darkie!' the rocks re-echoed. 'Wait for us. Wait for us. Wait for us.'

The bush boy turned. He knew what the call meant: the strangers were coming after him, were following him down the valley; already he could hear them crashing and lumbering through the scrub.

He waited; relaxed both physically and mentally: one hand passed behind his back and closed round the opposite elbow; one foot, ostrich-like, resting on the calf of the opposite leg. He wasn't frightened, for he knew instinctively that the strangers were harmless as a pair of tail-less kangaroos; but he *was* mildly surprised, for he had thought them both, especially the larger, impatient, eager to be on their way. As the children came racing towards him, he dropped his foot to the ground, became suddenly all attention; full of curiosity to know what they wanted to say and how they were going to say it.

Peter launched into a breathless appeal.

'Hey, don't leave us, darkie! We're lost. We want food, an' drink. And we wanna know how we get to Adelaide.'

Mary looked at the bush boy, and saw in his eyes a gleam of amusement. It angered her, for she knew the cause; Peter's high-pitched, corncrakey voice. All the tenets of progressive society and racial superiority combined inside her to form a deep-rooted core of resentment. It was wrong, cruelly wrong, that she and her brother should be forced to run for help to a Negro, and a naked Negro at that. She clutched Peter's hand, half drawing him away.

But Peter was obsessed by none of his sister's scruples. To him their problem was simple, uncomplicated: they wanted help, and here was someone who could, his instinct told him, provide it.

Picnic in Jammu

ZULFIKAR GHOSE

Uncle Ayub swung me round and round
till the horizon became a rail
banked high upon the Himalayas.
The trees signalled me past. I whistled,
shut my eyes through tunnels of the air.
The family laughed, watching me puff
out my muscles, healthily aggressive.

This was late summer, before the snows
come to Kashmir, this was picnic time.

Then, uncoupling me from the sky, he
plunged me into the river, himself
a bough with me dangling at its end.
I went purple as a plum. He reared
back and lowered the branch of his arm
to grandma who swallowed me with a kiss.
Laughter peeled away my goosepimples.

    This was late summer, before the snows
    come to Kashmir, this was picnic time.

After we'd eaten, he aimed grapes at
my mouth. I flung at him the shells of
pomegranates and ran off. He tracked
me down the river-bank. We battled,
melon-rind and apple-core our arms.
'You two!' grandma cried. 'Stop fighting, you'll
tire yourselves to death!' We didn't listen.

    This was late summer, before the snows
    come to Kashmir and end children's games.

Slake's Limbo

FELICE HOLMAN

> Slake is an undersized, dreamy, short-sighted boy who lives with an uncaring aunt in a slummy New York apartment. Here, he has taken the subway (the underground train system) to escape the gang who regularly bully him. And he has spent his last subway token.

He came up on to the street in a neighbourhood that he had never seen before, walked two blocks uptown to the splendid width of Seventy-ninth Street, and started to walk westward. Here were sparkling shops, large clean buildings, and neatly tended saplings along the edge of the relatively unlittered pavement. The absence of tin cans, garbage, and other refuse, the scarcity of steps and stoops, and the lack of people sitting or leaning about them interested Slake. As he crossed Park Avenue he waited on the kerb with respect as a young delivery boy drove a bicycle through heavy traffic as if it were a fine car. He continued along Seventy-ninth and finally crossed Fifth Avenue and walked into the autumn landscape of Central Park.

At the sight of the park, something came back to Slake. It was the recurrence of an old fantasy that *this year the leaves would stay on the trees.* Though there were few trees in Slake's life, this thought returned to him year after year. Now he broke into a run, winding and spinning through paths of the park, kicking up a kaleidoscope of fallen leaves, while above some leaves remained tenuously on the branches. Slake ran twenty blocks south, and well into the park. He was far from home … far from home, but his failing faith had given way once again to hope … a last hope. Slake, without sweater or subway token, put his faith in nature.

'This is the year ...,' said Slake as he ran, '*this* is the year the leaves *will* stay on the trees.' And the enthusiasm of this hope in this new territory, and the momentary strength of this conviction made Slake heady. He looked about quickly and saw only an old lady dozing on a bench. Her mouth was open; her hair looked borrowed. Slake grabbed a bunch of tall dried grass from the foot of a poorly tended maple tree, leaped into its low branches and, squinting against the sun, tied several of the remaining leaves securely to the branches.

That was Slake at the tallest, strongest moment of his life till then. It lasted *just* a moment. Shouts broke into his ambitious dream as a park attendant appeared, running, shouting, and waving a rake.

'Get down out of there, you bum kid!'

Slake blinked.

'Get down, I said!' The attendant poked at the tree with his rake, but Slake had moved out of reach. 'The cops, then!' and the man was off and running to a nearby phone. The old lady awoke and started pointing.

Slake, now entirely ripped from his dream, abandoned it on the branch, leaped to the ground, spun round twice, ran several hundred yards through the park and out of it, down a flight of stairs and, committing still another crime, ran frantic and tokenless under the turnstile and into the subway at Columbus Circle.

He stayed one hundred and twenty-one days.

Mum, Dad and Me

James Berry

My parents grew among palmtrees,
in sunshine strong and clear.
I grow in weather that's pale,
misty, watery or plain cold,
around back streets of London.

Dad swam in warm sea, at my age.
I swim in a roofed pool,
Mum – she still doesn't swim.

Mum went to an open village market
at my age. I go to a covered
arcade one with her now.
Dad works most Saturdays.

At my age Dad played
cricket with friends.
Mum helped her mum, or talked
shouting halfway up a hill.
Now I read or talk on the phone.

With her friends Mum's mum washed
clothes on a river-stone. Now
washing-machine washes our clothes.
We save time to eat to TV,
never speaking.

My dad longed for a freedom in Jamaica.
I want a greater freedom.
Mum prays for us, always.

Mum goes to church
some evenings and Sundays.
I go to the library.
Dad goes for his darts at the local.

Mum walked everywhere, at my age.
Dad rode a donkey.
Now I take a bus
or catch the underground train.

Hiawatha

HENRY WADSWORTH LONGFELLOW

> One hundred and fifty years ago, Longfellow
> (an American poet) wrote a long narrative poem
> about a legendary native American hero called
> Hiawatha. This is a small part of that poem.

Swift of foot was Hiawatha;
He could shoot an arrow from him,
And run forward with such fleetness,
That the arrow fell behind him!
Strong of arm was Hiawatha;
He could shoot ten arrows upward,
Shoot them with such strength and swiftness,
That the tenth had left the bowstring
Ere the first to earth had fallen!

There is more about legendary heroes on pages 55, 60 and 99.

Hiawatha

ADAPTED FOR THE STAGE BY MICHAEL BOGDANOV

HIAWATHA Give me of your bark, O Birch-Tree!
      I a light canoe will build me,
      That shall float upon the river,
      Like a yellow leaf in Autumn,
      Like a yellow water-lily!

*The main trunk should remain upright and
HIAWATHA makes canoe in front of it.*

STORY-TELLER With his knife the tree he girdled;
      Down the trunk, from top to bottom,
      Sheer he cleft the bark asunder,
      Stripped it from the trunk unbroken.

HIAWATHA Give me of your boughs, O Cedar!
      My canoe to make more steady,
      Make more strong and firm beneath me!

STORY-TELLER Through the summit of the Cedar
      Went a sound, a cry of horror,
      But it whispered, bending downward,

ONE Take my boughs, O Hiawatha!

STORY-TELLER Down he hewed the boughs of cedar,
      Shaped them straightway to a framework,
      Like two bows he formed and shaped them,
      Like two bended bows together.

HIAWATHA Give me of your roots, O Tamarack!
      My canoe to bind together,
      That the water may not enter.

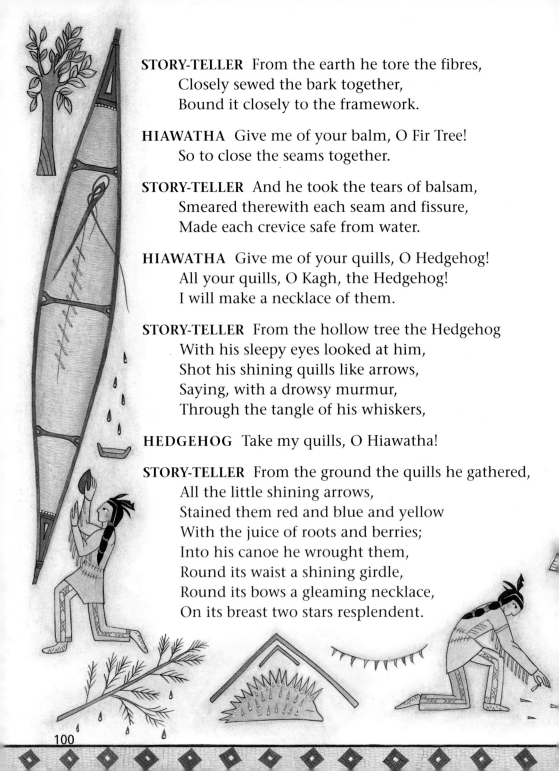

STORY-TELLER From the earth he tore the fibres,
Closely sewed the bark together,
Bound it closely to the framework.

HIAWATHA Give me of your balm, O Fir Tree!
So to close the seams together.

STORY-TELLER And he took the tears of balsam,
Smeared therewith each seam and fissure,
Made each crevice safe from water.

HIAWATHA Give me of your quills, O Hedgehog!
All your quills, O Kagh, the Hedgehog!
I will make a necklace of them.

STORY-TELLER From the hollow tree the Hedgehog
With his sleepy eyes looked at him,
Shot his shining quills like arrows,
Saying, with a drowsy murmur,
Through the tangle of his whiskers,

HEDGEHOG Take my quills, O Hiawatha!

STORY-TELLER From the ground the quills he gathered,
All the little shining arrows,
Stained them red and blue and yellow
With the juice of roots and berries;
Into his canoe he wrought them,
Round its waist a shining girdle,
Round its bows a gleaming necklace,
On its breast two stars resplendent.

Indian sign language is painted on the upright trunk to depict the images that follow. Flute.

ONE Thus the Birch Canoe was builded

TWO In the valley by the river,

THREE In the shadow of the forest;

FOUR And the forest's life was in it,

FIVE All its mystery and magic,

SIX All the lightness of the birch-tree,

SEVEN All the toughness of the cedar,

EIGHT All the larch's supple sinews.

HIAWATHA kneels at head of canoe.

HIAWATHA CANOE SONG
    Gu YoWan
    Ne Ho Ne Ho
    Gu Yo Wan A Nee E Ho
    Gu Yo Wan A Ne Ho

STORY-TELLER And it floated on the river
    Like a yellow leaf in Autumn,
    Like a yellow water-lily.

There is more about legendary heroes on pages 55, 60 and 98.

Storytime

JUDITH NICHOLLS

Once upon a time, children,
there lived a fearsome dragon …

Please miss,
Jamie's made a dragon.
Out in the sandpit.

Lovely, Andrew.
Now this dragon
had enormous red eyes
and a swirling, whirling tail …

Jamie's dragon's got
yellow eyes, miss.

Lovely, Andrew.
Now this dragon was
as wide as a horse
as green as the grass
as tall as a house …

Jamie's would JUST fit
in our classroom, miss!

But he was a very
    friendly dragon …

Jamie's dragon ISN'T, miss.
He eats people, miss.
Especially TEACHERS,
Jamie said.

Very nice, Andrew!
Now one day, children,
this enormous dragon
rolled his red eye,
whirled his swirly green tail
and set off to find …

His dinner, miss!
Because he was hungry, miss!

Thank you, Andrew.
He rolled his red eye,
whirled his green tail,
and opened his wide, wide mouth
until ooooooouuaaah!
Please miss,
I did try to tell you, miss!

There is more about dragons on pages 22, 23 and 76.

...The Cake That Makes You Scream!

DAVE WARD

Underneath the icing,
Underneath the cream,
Underneath the marzipan
Is the cake that makes you scream.

It's filled with sticky spiders,
Slugs and earwigs too,
And swarms of tiny beetles
Swimming round in glue.

Underneath the icing,
Underneath the cream,
Underneath the marzipan
Is the cake that makes you scream.

It's filled with vampires' fingernails
And all their fingers too,
Crawling from the oozing sludge
Just to tickle you.

Underneath the icing,
Underneath the cream,
Underneath the marzipan
Is the cake that makes you scream.

It's filled with twisted nightmares
Where strawberries turn blue,
And fishes' legs and donkey eggs
Growl and howl and moo.

Underneath the icing,
Underneath the cream,
Underneath the marzipan
Is the cake that makes you scream.

When you cut this curious cake
You don't know what you'll find;
Be careful or the slimy jam
Will climb inside your mind.

But even more important,
Be careful with the knife:
It'll try and slice your tongue out
Before you can take a bite.

Then you won't taste the icing,
And you won't taste the cream,
And the marzipan will slobber out
In a sickening, shapeless scream.

The Editor
The Casterbridge Journal

April 30th 2000

Mrs J A Booth
Roseview
Manor Road
Casterbridge

Dear Sir,

Thank you for having the courage to print the article 'Our Children Are Becoming Couch Potatoes'. I could not agree more. Like most people, I am horrified by the enormous amount of time children spend watching television and playing their computer games. As a mother and grandmother, I know for a fact that families do not talk to each other or even sit together to share the evening meal. Is there anything more horrible than eating off trays in front of the television?

My grandchildren have televisions and Play Centres in their rooms, and this makes conversation impossible. The so-called 'games' children play on their computers are violent and unintelligent, and the truth is that the programmes shown on television before children's bedtime are mostly American rubbish.

But this is not the main problem. The main problem is that children do not get enough exercise. When I was a girl, I cycled the two miles to school each day. Cycling is a good form of exercise, and so is walking. These days, parents drive their children to school in cars. Last week I took my grandchildren to school and watched the others arrive. Less than half the children came by bicycle or on foot. Why? And when they are at school they do not do half the P.E. that we used to do.

So what is the answer? I'm sure that your readers would agree that there is only one answer: we must spend more time together as families, and we must ration the amount of time children spend in front of 'the box'. And, of course, we must stop acting as their taxi-drivers.

Yours faithfully,

Mrs J. A. Booth

Mr M. Reynolds   A. M. Lal
Head Teacher, Exeter Rd School   47 Bridge St
Budmouth   Budmouth

April 2nd 2000

Dear Mr Reynolds,

As you know, I have two children at your school. I have noticed lately that
they have more homework to do. Personally, I do not think that homework
is a good thing; I believe that work should be done at school, and that the
home should be a place for family life. I understand that we all want our
children to do well, and if you think that homework is necessary, then I will
accept it. The point I want to make is this: home is not the best place to
do homework. Here are some of my reasons for thinking so:

- Home is full of distractions: the telephone, the television, people
  coming to visit, and so on.
- Homework can cause arguments and bad feelings; doing homework
  can seem like a punishment, and this is a bad thing.
- Many homes do not have the things that help children with their
  homework. Many do not have a computer and lots of books and so on.
- It is unfair when, for example, a child has to do an English homework
  and his parents do not speak English very well. They cannot help him.
  This means that children whose parents speak good English and have
  books and computers and so on will have a big advantage.

What is the answer to this problem? It is, I think, this: do the homework at
school. If my children have two hours homework each week, then they
should stay at school to do it. They would have the help of the teacher
and also use of the school library and computers. There would be none of
the distractions of home. They would do the work more quickly, and when
they came home they could relax. Please consider my suggestion
seriously and let me know what you think about it.

Yours sincerely,

A. M. Lal

*Good
Looking*

Vision. And Pure Magic.

A beautiful painting deserves a beautiful frame.
And just as a frame draws attention to a picture,
beautiful eyelashes draw attention to the beauty of your eyes.
The artists who have created Pure Magic mascara
have found their inspiration in the richness of black velvet and the
shimmering sheen of black pearls.

Pure Magic. It's not make-up. It's what you deserve.

Mark Tully reports from India on the pioneering work
being done there to treat cataract.

When I was a child I often woke up panic-stricken in the middle
of the night. Terrified that I was blind, I would search
desperately for the light switch and reassurance.
I still sometimes find myself groping anxiously
for the bedside light when I'm staying in a strange
hotel. Fear of blindness is my worst nightmare,
as it is, I know, for many others. Yet although
sight is so precious, there are more than 35
million blind people in the world who could
see. The problem is not just providing the
treatment but letting the blind know that
it is available, and persuading them
that it is safe. That is just what is
being done now in India. ■

Second Sight campaign leaflet

Old Macdonald had a farm ...

... and on that farm he has some chickens

ANIMAL AID CAMPAIGN LEAFLET

...90,000 of them – held in two massive sheds. It's on this scale that most chickens are reared today in the UK. 45,000 in one vast, windowless shed is not uncommon; the birds shoulder to shoulder, struggling to make it to the watering and feeding stations. Many don't succeed. They die from starvation or dehydration. All kinds of other problems carry off thousands more of Old Mac's chickens every year before they can be slaughtered. These problems include – and they're common throughout the industry – heat stress, heart attacks, fatty liver and kidney disease, and a devastating viral complaint sometimes known as 'chicken AIDS'. Amazingly, a lot of the public – scared by BSE – are running to chicken as a 'health food'.

Throughout the trade, deaths in sheds run to about 6 per cent or more. The victims rot where they fall, since sheds aren't cleaned out until all the birds are grown and are ready for transportation to the killing plants. This journey happens when they're just six weeks old. Such rapid growth, spurred by the use of chemical 'growth promoters', is part of the reason the birds are so prone to disease and also to fractured and broken legs; their limbs aren't strong enough to hold their unnaturally huge bodies.

The end of Madconald's chickens is signalled by the arrival of the freelance catching gang – six men who grab the birds by the feet and thrust them into crates, which get loaded onto slaughter lorries.

Chicken Brained

MILES KINGTON

In every frozen chicken
You'll find a little bag,
Tucked neatly in the ribcage,
And fastened with a tag.

This extra little parcel
Most thoughtfully contains
Its liver, neck and kidney,
But not its chicken brains.

For the normal farmyard chicken
Is the dumbest bird you'll find
And it's just not worth preserving
Its tiny little mind.

Style and Feature Links

Anthropomorphism
The Spider and the Fly 70
Cool Cat 73
The Private Life of the Otter 74

Comic horror
Jabberwocky 16
The Wendigo 19
Things that go Bump
    in the Night 58
The Cake That Makes You
    Scream 104

Myths and legends
Dracula 12
The Eggs Cracks 54
Beowulf 55
King Arthur 60
Hiawatha 98

Narrative Poems
Jabberwocky 16
To Find a Son and Heir 52
The Fox 68
The Spider and the Fly 70
Hiawatha 98

Observing Animals
Running Lightly Over Spongy
    Ground 24
The Private Life of the Otter 74
A London Evacuee sees
    his First Cow 78
The Silken Trap 82

Playscripts
Twopence to Cross the Mersey 26
Skungpoomery 30
Hiawatha 99

Refrains
The Fox 68
Picnic in Jammu 92
The Cake That Makes You
    Scream 104

Story Openings
Bill's New Frock 6
Nightmare Stairs 7
Treasure Island 8
Goodnight Mr Tom 10
When Hitler Stole Pink Rabbit 84